The Turkish Diplomat's Daughter

The Turkish Diplomat's Daughter

Deniz Goran

First published 2007.

A Burning House book.

www.burninghousebooks.com

Burning House is an imprint of
Beautiful Books Limited
117 Sugden Road
London SW11 5ED

ISBN 9781905636129

9 8 7 6 5 4 3 2 1

A catalogue reference for this book is available from the British Library.

Cover design by Ian Pickard.
Printed in Great Britain by MacKays of Chatham.

To Antonio, for believing in me.
To Ufuk, for encouraging me.
And to Fırfır, for comforting me.

1

The Sailor

Until that summer, I never had the balls to pursue any of my sexual fantasies. It wasn't because virginity was a big issue for me, that is, in the conventional sense. For some peculiar reason while I was growing up, making the path from childhood to adulthood, that confusingly frustrating path we all take, I never felt comfortable with my own sexuality. Although I remember that from the age of eight I masturbated nearly every other day, seeing the first string of pubic hair, feeling the two discomforting lumps on my flat chest, and especially coming face to face with the first traces of blood stains on my white cotton panties, disgusted and scared the shit out of me. Hair, lumps and blood. What was happening to me? Okay, I sort of knew what was going on but I just wasn't ready for it. My body was changing and I had no control over it whatsoever. I was literally turning into one of those women I so often came across while flicking through my Father's dirty magazines. Was my Father aware of the two small lumps on my chest? I so hoped that he wasn't. Even when I finally adjusted to my monthly periods, my thick dark strands of pubic hair and the two fully grown lumps on my chest, I suspected, for some reason, that I was sexually disabled. Like what if my vagina was in fact blocked and I was unable to technically have intercourse with a man? I remember going to a gynaecologist in Rome before deciding to lose my virginity. When she had asked me why I was there I had nervously replied, 'I just want you to check and see if everything is normal down there.' After giving me an awkward look she asked me to remove all my clothing from the waist down and as I lay down with my legs spread wide apart, watching the ceiling while a complete stranger was fiddling with my bits, my mind was jumping from one thought to another:

Oh my God! I am at a gynaecologist, it's so exciting! This is my first step to womanhood... I hate myself for having a vagina. It makes me feel dirty. Would I've preferred to have a penis instead? Well, not really. At the end of the day, it's the same shit in reverse; like having a vagina inside out. Maybe being sexless would've been the best option. But then wouldn't that make me a freak? I guess there is no ultimate solution to the problem... I wonder if my vagina looks distinctively different from anyone else's? It probably doesn't, as I didn't see a hint of terror in her eyes when she came face to face with it. But what if it's all a part of being a professional? Maybe she's just putting on an act? She must be a lesbian. Even if she isn't there must be something seriously wrong with her. Or else, why would she want to stare at pussies for the rest of her life? Or maybe she was a lesbian but became straight after being exposed to too many pussies and now it's too late for her to change professions and she's depressed... How can you be so shallow? The woman is a doctor for crying out loud! She's a lifesaver. Maybe you should get your head checked, instead of your pussy!

After examining me for ten minutes or so she told me to get up and get dressed and added that everything was fine with me. I started to quickly dress myself with a slight feeling of guilt towards her.

My first experience of sexual intercourse had been anything but pleasurable. Well, now looking back at it, it had actually felt more like having a smear test than anything else. Highly discomforting, awkward and embarrassing. I guess it's only natural when even the thought of a man's large penis entering that tiny hole between your legs sends shivers down your spine.

Nevertheless, whether it's your first kiss or your first shag, movies can also have a seriously misguiding effect. You see, until then you've already watched enough adult intimacy scenes that way before you experience your first kiss or shag, you naturally have a cinematic version of how it's going to turn out. Let's take the first kiss for example. You are in a dimly lit setting. Like on a beach beneath the stars, or in front of a fireplace. He grabs you by the waist with his strong muscular arms and in return you pretend to resist by attempting to slightly push him away. This only makes him want you even more. You can hear your favourite theme song playing softly in the background (my theme song used to be Prince's *When Doves Cry*). Then he looks straight into your eyes, presses his body against yours and sinks his lips into yours. And as the intensity of your kiss increases so does the volume of the music in the background. It's pure bliss… Whereas in cold reality, you're at his house, in his lousy room on a Saturday afternoon. He goes to the door to lock it carefully straight after his Mother has dropped off a tray of cookies and orange juice. He comes back and sits next to you, gives you a funny look and then hesitantly puts his arm over your shoulders. He leans closer and closer and as he does you suddenly notice the greasy black spots on his nose and a white pimple, just ready to pop out, right next to his upper lip. You remind yourself that now is probably a good time to close your eyes unless you want to end up cross-eyed or something. Then he kisses you. In the best cases, it feels soft and wet. You think to yourself, 'Is that it?' Yet once you get past your primal state of disillusion, separate life from illusion and venture into the never ending rich possibilities that real-life sexual intimacy has to offer (which no movie has ever or will ever be able to portray, in all its glory) you rarely look back.

Finally, that particular summer, I felt ready to experience the joys of my new self. To let go of my sexual inhibitions with the help of my fantasy man, the Sailor.

At the age of twelve, when I had arrived in Turkey from Canada for the very first time in the summer of '86, we spent the whole summer season at a certain seaside resort just outside Ayvalik[1], where my grandparents had a summerhouse and where my parents would later on own one of their own. Since then I had formed an infatuation for a sailor who was nine years my senior and who was also a distant relative on my Mother's side. Every summer, when he came over with his friends to help move my Father's fishing boat into the sea, I would gaze with admiration at his always tanned, muscular, tall and lean body and would almost melt inside when he came up and knelt beside me to ask how I was. For him, I was just a pretty little girl. For me, he was a primary source for masturbation. Just think of a rougher and less polished version of Brad Pitt and you'd have him. He had various scars on his face and had a

1 Ayvalik is a small seaside town by the Aegean coast.

distinctive jaw line that gave his otherwise feminine facial features a very masculine edge. Yet he still had the same blue narrowed eyes, small upturned nose and the same voluptuous, kissable lips. He would usually be strutting about all summer with a pair of burnt, torn, stained denim shorts and a pair of sneakers; that's all he ever wore. Whenever I told my Mother that I thought he was cute my Mother would grimace, as if I had just told her that I had the hots for some inmate and say, 'How could you ever fancy a person like that? He is a tramp, a low life. You must be joking!'

Yet I never had been more serious in my life. Yes, this sex god was in fact the black sheep of our family, yet for me that seemed to add to his appeal. He wasn't a boring pretty face but a troubled soul. He had been unable to finish high school and would spend most of the year working on ships, going from one port to another, gaining an extensive amount of knowledge on local spirits and cocktails, the majority of which most of us had not yet heard of. When he did get back home, usually sometime towards the summer, we would often enough hear of his numerous misconducts. Probably it was his own way of letting everyone know that he was back in town. His most common scenario would be that he'd get drunk, lose his temper and start up a fight and beat someone to near death, smash their face with a broken bottle and end up spending the rest of the night at a police station. Luckily his dad was an alcoholic lawyer who always found some intricate way of saving his troubled son's ass. Naturally, people were afraid of him. They would either try to avoid him in any way they could or simply stay completely silent in his presence. My cousin and his friends, who were all a bunch of adolescent boys that tried ever so hard to create a bad boy image, would show him a great deal of respect and try their very best to be on good terms with him. For them he was the epitome of coolness, like James Dean in *Rebel Without a Cause*, he was a guy who lived by his own rules: a misfit and an alcoholic who would beat up his girlfriends on a regular basis. And his so-called girlfriends were usually prostitutes that slept with him for free once they'd fallen for his good looks.

That summer, when I had spent a month at our summerhouse and had returned to Istanbul like a good little girl as soon as my parents had gone back to Rome, I had realised that finally the coast was clear: my parents were away, I was no longer a virgin; I had to make the most of it. The day after my parents left for Rome, I returned to Ayvalik with the keys to our empty summerhouse in my pocket. As soon as I arrived, I knew I had no time to waste; I spent the whole day looking for him. I went up to any remotely familiar face and asked if they had seen him around that day. Then around six o'clock in the afternoon, when I had just started to lose my faith after doing an extensive tour of the town, I finally saw him drinking a pint of beer at some bar by the sea. As I went up to him I said, 'Hi, I just got into town today and my parents are away; I have nothing to do tonight. Would you like to meet up and go for a bite or a drink later on?'

As soon as he replied I could tell that he was already reasonably tipsy. He said, 'Of course I'll take you out. I'll look after you, don't you worry. You know, you are family to me, you are like my little sister.'

Yes indeed, a little sister who wants to fuck your brains out tonight. Frankly, I didn't like the fact that he still saw me as some sort of a kid. After all, I hadn't travelled on a coach for six hours just to hear that, but I tried not to let it get to me. I had to be patient. We agreed to meet at the same spot two hours later. When I did return, after taking a long bath, shaving my legs and armpits and wearing a pink strapless summer dress, I found him where I had left him, drinking another pint of beer and having a chat with the bartender. As I approached him he looked up, blurry eyed, and said, 'You look nice. So, where would you like to go?'

I shrugged my shoulders and responded, 'I don't mind; anywhere is fine by me.'

'Anywhere?'

I nodded.

'So you're an uncomplicated girl, are you? Whereas I thought you'd be otherwise.'

I just gave him a shy smile and said, 'I'm always very easy to please,' which was nothing but a white lie.

First he took me to a fish restaurant by the sea, then to a local open-air bar.

'Are you sure you're not freezing in that skimpy dress?' he said as we were seated surrounded by olive trees and wandering stray cats while a local amateur band was playing old favourite Turkish tunes. I brought my body forward onto the only obstacle between us, an old wooden square table and rested both arms on top of it before gently biting my lower lip and then taking a sip from my bottle of beer.

'Actually on the contrary I feel quite hot,' I responded as I looked straight into his eyes and then said, in order to play down my seduction game just a little bit, 'I guess it must be the effect of the alcohol.'

'I'm really glad that you suggested that we meet up tonight.'

'Are you?' I asked as I lifted my eyebrows suggestively.

'It's funny how we're relatives and I've known you since you were a little girl; how old were you when you got back from Vancouver?'

'Twelve.'

'So I've known you since you were twelve; and now you're…?'

'Eighteen,' I responded proudly.

'Eighteen, ha? It's funny how time flies. Well anyway, what I'm trying to say is that we've never had a chance to get to know each other and I think that it's about time that that changed.'

'I couldn't agree with you more. So tell me a bit about yourself. Like, why did you become a sailor?'

'Why did I become a sailor?'

With the same bemused expression that a grown up would have when just about to answer the questions of an inquisitive youngster, he leaned his back against his chair and then replied, 'Because it gives me freedom. I didn't want to be tied down in Ayvalik or anywhere else for the rest of my life with a nine-to-five job. You see, ever since I was a little boy, all I wanted from life was to have this limitless freedom; a life where I could carry the least amount of responsibility, be a nomad and just cruise around the world. A life where I would be my own boss. You know, every year when I get back to Ayvalik in the beginning of the summer I'm glad at first to see my friends and family but literally after three or four months have passed by I start feeling restless again. I just want to go; I don't care where it is as long as it's far away from here.'

'Hmm.'

'What about you? What is it that you want to become?'

I gazed into the distance for a second and then replied, 'I haven't decided yet.'

And just as he was walking me home, while going on about some irrelevant thing as he was pissed out of his brains, I stopped him right in the middle of the road, grabbed his face firmly with my two hands and forced my tongue into his mouth. He gently pushed me away and said, with a surprised and amused look on his face, 'Wow, what are you doing? We cannot do that, I cannot do that; we're relatives.'

So what? It wasn't like he was my brother or cousin, and even cousins are allowed. I totally ignored what he'd just said and started to kiss him again. This time round he didn't push me away but said, after he finally had a chance to catch his breath, 'This is crazy. Your Grandfather would kill me if he ever found out.'

He was a nonconformist rebel, why did he care so much about what some seventy-year-old guy was going to say or do to him? I guess it was all a part of living in a small town; you had to somehow show a bit of respect for your elders if nothing else. You simply could not break all the rules, there were some rules that even misfits were reluctant to break, and I was tempting him.

When we came to the front of our summerhouse I was all over him again, thinking to myself, 'Boy, does this feel good.' You see, till that day I had made up endless scenarios in my mind about him. I won't give you the whole seductive layout in detail, but usually I imagined going out one night and coming across him by mere coincidence at a bar while enjoying myself with my friends. He would watch me all night long and would feel this uncontrollable desire to have me. As I would make my way to the bathroom he would follow me and then without saying a single word force himself onto me and start kissing me passionately. Okay, I had lived a slightly different version of my fantasy as I had been compelled to switch roles here, unless I wanted to wait forever that is, but still it felt so amazing that I was actually kissing him for real, for the first time.

During that previous month in Ayvalik spent with my parents he was all that I thought about. I was aroused just by the mere sensation of the wind hitting my body whenever I took a walk by the beach, imagining that instead it was his rough fingertips that were tickling me all over. When I left the house it was always with the intention of running into him and when I was ever lucky enough to do so I would just say, 'Hi, how's it going?' in a cool manner with a deep sexy voice and then go over to join my cousin and his friends while walking my sexy walk and putting on my sexy face. You see, as I was kissing him passionately on the veranda of our summerhouse overlooking the sea on that particular evening, I was well aware that I was finally prepared to accomplish one of the biggest challenges of my life. Yes, maybe I was transforming myself into one of those sexed-up women I so often came across in my Father's dirty magazines, yet it no longer felt dirty; it just felt natural.

Then I stopped and asked him if he'd like to come in for

a drink. He said that, really, he would love to but he simply couldn't, that it was all wrong.

'I promise that we'll just listen to some music and have a civilized drink.'

He just shook his head from side to side and then muttered, 'I really don't know…'

'No! You're coming in with me; end of story, and stop acting as if you have a choice,' I said as I dragged him through our front door. I knew that it was either now or never; he was drunk as a fish and I had to use it to my advantage. I could not possibly let him get away.

We were seated next to each other, holding onto our icy cold glasses of raki[2], listening to the melancholic melodies of a Sezen Aksu[3] album. After taking a large sip from my glass to wash away the discomforting taste of nicotine in my mouth, I slowly moved my body closer to him and started to gently stroke his hair and face.

He smiled and said, 'This is crazy.'

I asked, 'Good crazy or bad crazy?' in a playful manner.

He didn't answer back but just took a deep breath and stared lustfully into my eyes. As soon as I leaned forward and placed my lips against his, I felt his warm, slippery tongue enter my mouth. It was a substitute for his manhood, as it tried to reach

2 Raki is our national alcoholic beverage. It's always served in a thin cylindrical glass. Although raki is a clear drink, it becomes milky when water is added because it contains aniseed; hence it also goes by the name of lion's milk.

3 Turkish pop diva (dubbed the little sparrow for having such a spectacular, smoky voice) who has been reigning over the Turkish pop music scene for decades. She's one of the rare musicians in Turkey who can break barriers and actually appeal to people from every walk of life.

each and every corner of my mouth fervently. While he was poking his tongue back and forth into my mouth, I quickly slipped my hands through his denim shorts so as to get a feel of his erect penis. Then as I moved my hands on top of his shorts and was just about to unzip for easy access he distanced himself from me. He looked into my eyes, while breathing heavily, and said, 'Are you sure you want to do this? It's too dangerous. We might end up getting ourselves into a bigger mess than we could ever imagine.'

'Well, that's the main attraction for me,' I thought to myself but just smiled back at him. You know when you're just about too drunk to walk in a straight line yet all of a sudden get things in a clearer perspective? Well I was having that moment. Nonetheless I didn't want to rationalize my behaviour; I just wanted to let go. I got up, held his hand and guided him to my parents' bedroom. It was quite funny in a way, that even when we were naked in my parents' bed and he was on top of me, he was still going on about how wrong this was. I told him to stop nagging and just get on with it; it was too late to have second thoughts.

The next morning as he woke up and lifted his head off the pillow, he smiled and said,

'I really can't believe I am here, lying in your parents' bed all naked.'

I told him that being naked really suited him, that I wanted to see him more often like that, and I really meant it. He smiled awkwardly and got up. I watched his back, his narrow hips, his round firm ass, his long muscular legs and his broad shoulders, as he made his way to the bathroom. No, I thought to myself, it definitely wasn't a mistake. When he was getting dressed and I was still in bed smoking a cigarette and admiring the view, I told him that I wanted to see him again that night. He said, 'Okay,' in a thoughtful manner.

It was kind of cute that I had brought out a different side in him; I doubt that he had ever thought about the consequences of any of his actions until then.

Later that day I met up with my cousin to tell him what I had been up to the night before. For years he had put up with me going on and on about how sexy I thought the Sailor was, and how one day I was determined to have him. He picked me up in his red Alfa Romeo sports car and as soon as I got in I gave him the good news, to make him aware that I wasn't all talk and no action.

'I've done it at last.'

'Done what at last?'

'My sole mission in life. I finally slept with him.'

'Slept with who?'

'What's wrong with you? Haven't you had your morning coffee yet?'

'You mean you've slept with…'

I nodded with a big grin on my face and then shouted as I lifted both hands up in the air:

'Goal, goal! Yes ladies and gentlemen, the ball has finally entered the back of the net. He was amazing. You know we did it…'

'Just spare me the details, all right? You don't know what you're getting yourself into. You seriously have to watch yourself with him. What if he becomes obsessed with you and doesn't want to let you go once you've had your fun with him? You know, he's a dangerous guy and he can hurt you. A couple of months ago, I heard from a few people that he beat the living daylights out of one of his girlfriends before throwing her out on the street all naked. He's sick you know and you are asking for trouble.'

I was disappointed that he saw my keen interest in the Sailor as some sort of carefree amusement that was destined to lead to no good. Naturally he had a point, but you know how frustrating it is when you've just had an intense, earthshaking experience and the first person you confide in goes ahead and ruins it all by being rational and mature. That really pisses me off. I told him that he was being way too paranoid and that the Sailor would never lay a finger on me. I wasn't like the cheap prostitutes he slept around with; I was family and therefore was going to be treated differently.

The truth of the matter is, although he was a distant relative of ours he had always looked up to, and respected, my parents and my grandparents. He was well aware that neither he nor his parents were in the same league as us. He had actually never been invited to our house as a guest. My Father would ask him to drop by occasionally when he needed an extra hand with his boat. The Sailor would act completely unlike his usual self, being very polite and well-mannered to such an extent that he would make it way too obvious that he was just faking it. Once he was done with the job he would leave, as my parents rarely invited him for a cup of tea or coffee and even when they did he knew that they were just being polite. My parents, especially my Mother, can come across as being a bit reserved and snobbish at times. But I also have to admit that his bad boy image had a lot to do with it. Family or no family, my mum basically did not want to associate herself with a violent, alcoholic misfit. She had known him since he was a baby and had witnessed how such an innocent creature had transformed into a destructive, abusive monster. She already had enough on her plate dealing with my Father, and unlike me, she wasn't looking for more trouble.

Although it was a big deal for me to have him between my legs on that very first night, for him it was an even bigger deal, almost a privilege to spend the night at our place. After he got over his initial guilt trip, he was so amazed that I, a diplomat's daughter who was supposed to be dating some well-educated rich brat from Istanbul who put on half a jar of hair gel and soaked himself in Fahrenheit Aftershave before going out to roam the city with his brand new flashy sports car, had chosen him instead. He kept asking, 'Why do you want me?'

As I found it difficult being completely frank with him I'd be diplomatic with the whole thing and reply to his question with another question by simply saying, 'Why shouldn't I?' After all, I was a diplomat's daughter.

Whenever I saw him it was impossible to keep my hands off him. And I couldn't care less about where we were or if anyone was watching. It was as if there was some kind of chemical attraction between my right hand and his penis; I constantly felt the need to touch it and play with it. It was he who kept reminding me that we needed to be discreet. Usually we would come across certain family members or friends of the family while buying food from a local Bakkal[4] or sunbathing on the beach. I really didn't care one bit about people finding out. Like the night we had gone to a cemetery with a few drunken friends of his to pay our tributes to some dead poet, I grabbed hold of him and dragged him to some far corner of the dark bushy cemetery, only to give him a thorough, extended blowjob. Although his initial reaction would be, 'What are you doing? No, no, we can't do it here!' he would soon let himself go and moan with pleasure. He certainly was something.

Did my physical animalistic attraction for him bear any level of emotional depth? To be quite honest with you, I was way too blinded by my infatuation to really be totally aware of what I felt for him. All I can say is that I wasn't just drawn to his good looks but the whole package. At the end of the day, he wasn't some handsome dumb guy who had nothing to say about anything. Maybe he hadn't finished high school, but he had self educated himself by reading extensively when he was away at sea.

'Who's your favourite author?' I asked, as we strutted along the seaside both dressed in denim shorts, white T-shirts and sneakers.

'It's hard to say. Nabokov perhaps. *Lolita* is such an amazing novel. Have you ever read it?'

'Yes', I replied with excitement and then continued, 'It's one of my favourites as well 'cause Humbert Humbert's character

4 A Bakkal is a small shop packed with anything you can find in a supermarket. I always prefer to shop from a Bakkal when I'm in Turkey as it's a more intimate and cosy affair. Like if you'd ever forget to take your purse with you, the owner would simply give you a warm smile and say that you can pay him later. Try doing that in London. Having said that, nowadays Bakkals are like endangered species as large food store chains are replacing them.

is so complex that you're never able to totally disapprove of the guy. Despite the fact that you know that what he's doing is wrong you're still able to empathize with him. I think it's because Nabokov is able to portray him so well as this middle-aged pervert and a man in love at the same time; he's able to show us that nothing in life is black and white after all.'

'Or maybe you just liked the novel because you're also a Lolita yourself; a young seductress?'

'Na, I'm too old to be a Lolita.'

He wasn't the monster everyone thought him to be either, at least not towards me. In fact he had a very delicate, sensitive soul that he had been concealing behind his aggressive, violent ways. Throughout our intense two-month romance he never laid a finger on me. Sometimes I would test his limits by slapping him really hard on the face while sitting on his lap, knowing that it was something that would easily set anybody off, including myself. First he would ask me to kindly stop doing it and if I didn't listen, which was usually the case, he would simply grab hold of my hands and not let go for a minute or two.

A week into our relationship my Grandmother called me up and asked me to drop by. I went over to her house, a ten minute walk from ours, that same afternoon. My grandparents were the pillars of society in the small town of Ayvalik. My Grandfather had arrived there with his family at the ripe old age of thirteen from the pre-Ottoman occupied territory of former Yugoslavia and had struggled and worked like a slave from an early age onwards to create his little empire. He owned a factory that produced soap and cleaning products, a gas station, a car showroom as well as numerous properties that he rented out. Nevertheless he was the stingiest person I ever came into contact with in my life. My Mother would always mention how difficult it was for her while growing up, as her Father was unwilling to provide the basics for his children regardless of the fact that he was one of the most successful entrepreneurs in town. How she would be left feeling ashamed as a young girl next to her peers, always having to wear the most outdated, unflattering outfits. As my Grandfather grew older, his stinginess grew stronger. I remember that about a decade before his death he became particularly fixated with the notion of water conservation. At first he became reluctant to water the garden on a regular basis, then gave up on it completely and finally he broke the toilet in their house so that it would no longer flush.

My Grandmother on the other hand was a highly generous and social person who loved to have friends over for tea all day long. She was never short of any guests. She would hide the trays of freshly baked cakes and pastries that she had prepared for them under the bed in one of the spare bedrooms until my Grandfather went to work. Nevertheless, now and again, when my Grandfather returned home in the evening to find my Grandmother sitting in their living room with her friends he would quietly disappear to switch off the central power unit to make everybody fully aware that it was time to make a move. When I once asked her how she had been able to put up with my Grandfather's ways she had replied, 'In life you always have to put up with something so I got used to it and learned to play along with it. I was happy with your Grandfather for thirty-one years until the day I found out that he was having an affair with another woman. I could never forgive him for that.'

She did, however, and when my Grandfather eventually passed away, it took her over two years to recover and get her life back together.

As I opened the front gate and made my way through the long, wide, cemented pathway, which was adorned by a mixture of summer flowers and fruit trees on either side, I saw her sitting by the veranda knitting away. When I got closer she noticed me and looked up. My Grandmother had always been a very easy-going, sweet-natured and warm-hearted person; one of those rare breeds of people that are too good for their own sake. Yet, when I went over and gave her a kiss on the cheek she seemed rather distant, and almost not pleased to see me at all. I asked her if everything was okay to which she replied, 'No, not really.'

I said, 'What's the matter?'

She replied, without lifting her head up. 'Reputation is one of the most important qualities for a young girl and the way you conduct yourself does not only affect your own reputation but also that of your family. Luckily, I had no problems in that department with your Mother. She always knew how to carry herself and guard herself from the evil that is out there. Look at her now; she is happily married to a wonderful man.'

Yes, to an obnoxious diplomat, I thought to myself. Then she continued, 'You can't just do as you please; you have to think of your future.'

I knew where this was all heading so I asked her to stop beating around the bush and just spit it out. She told me that she had been hearing some rumours about the Sailor and I. To that day

I had never been in any way mean or unpleasant towards her but you have to understand that at that stage I was completely overtaken by my affair and could not allow any form of interference. So, I became defensive and explained, raising my voice at her, that yes, I was hanging out with him, and what exactly was the problem? She said that he had been a disgrace to our family. He was a lunatic, a tramp. Why would I possibly want to spend time with such a person? She hesitantly looked up at me and asked, 'Did he harm you in anyway?' That was a discreet way of asking if I had slept with him. I was furious and told her that no, he hadn't harmed me; we were just good friends and she had no right to put her nose where it did not belong. After all I didn't want to give the old lady a heart attack.

I was totally unaware that in a matter of a week our relationship had become the event of the moment for the inquisitive residents of Ayvalik. In that particular week, the rise in inflation or the horrific PKK[5] attacks in the Southeast had all lost their relevance. Unintentionally I had helped these people forget about their usual day-to-day concerns. In contrast to big cities like Istanbul or Ankara, Ayvalik didn't offer an endless range of hiding grounds. Ayvalik then, was limited to two tea gardens, one cheesy discotheque, five restaurants and four bars. And whenever you turned up at any of these venues you would come across the

5 PKK is a Kurdish terrorist group. They want a piece of our land and we ain't giving it to them so thousands and thousands of people have to die. The majority of the Kurdish population in Turkey resides in the Southeast and when taking into account their poverty-stricken lives (as none of the ruling governments have ever tried to develop the Southeast region, economically or culturally) you can't really blame them. But then again I can never sympathise with the idea that killing defenseless people is the correct way to get your message across.

same curious faces. I suddenly realised that I had never once seen a Turkish couple kiss or fondle each other in public there. That's why my cousin and me used to spy on German tourists over the summer to see a bit of live action when we were kids. In a small town like Ayvalik the last thing you wanted to do was draw attention to yourself.

Soon enough I was to find out the difficulties of having an unconventional and passionate love affair in a little town where the term privacy does not exist. You simply can't misbehave and if you do, you are constantly reminded that you just have. It can seriously get on your nerves. Once you understand how little towns function, how everybody knows each other's dirty business and that you have to either not have a life or put up with what people have to say about you, or worse, be very, very tactical about disguising your own shit, then you realise it's time to take your affair elsewhere. So I decided that we should go to Istanbul before I turned into some sort of a paranoid freak, whose primary concern in life was what people thought or had to say about her.

When we arrived in Istanbul we were able to reclaim our anonymity and do as we pleased. At nights he would either cook for me (he had learnt how to cook while working on board and was a reasonably good cook) or he would take me out for a meal to some rundown restaurant by the sea in Ortakoy[6] or an old Meyhane[7], and we would have fish along with a bottle of

6 Ortakoy is a district by the European shores of Istanbul, famous for its nightlife.

7 Meyhanes are cheap, rundown restaurants where there's always some depressingly lousy old Turkish music playing in the background. Your main objective at a Meyhane is to get blind drunk. If you are a bohemian intellectual or an alcoholic looking for some cheap booze, it's the place for you.

raki, get completely pissed and then collapse in bed just after one last session of screwing each other's brains out.

One early evening while watching the sunset together from my balcony overlooking the Bosphorus he said, 'Everybody in our family thinks that I am a loser but I'm going to prove them wrong. You'll see.'

I sincerely replied, 'Well, I'm not one of them.'

Not seeming totally convinced he continued, 'But I have only myself to blame. I hated going to school, being told what to do. I felt like being locked in a cage whenever I entered the classroom. I wanted to live by my own rules and do as I pleased. But soon enough you reach a certain stage in life when you realise that you can never really do as you please without paying a price.'

'Then why don't you go back to school and get your high school diploma? You can even do a degree after that. It's never too late...you're only twenty seven.'

'It is for me. I'm just too used to living the life I have led. Like, imagine that you bought a puppy and never trained it... it's too late to tame me.'

He took a drag from his cigarette while staring at the orange purple sky that was reflecting on the calm waters of the Bosphorus and then turned round to me and said, 'You're a smart girl and you can really make something out of your life. I'm talking to you like a big brother now. You'd never have thought you'd hear such words coming from me, right?'

I smiled and rolled my eyes. I really wasn't up for a lecture.

'I know you. Like me you're a free spirit,' he said.

I have to admit that I also saw a bit of him in me. Yet I

couldn't relate to why he was reluctant to make any changes in his life, regardless of the fact that he wasn't really happy with how things had turned out so far. Above all, it was he who considered himself to be a loser. And although he strutted down the narrow streets of Ayvalik with his chin high up and shoulders firmly back, as if he owned the place, and had the power to intimidate anyone that crossed his path, he still didn't have the emotional strength to make a fresh start.

There seems to be a certain mysterious air attached to the whole image of being a free spirit, a rebel without a cause. Let me just point out to you that there is no such thing as a rebel without a cause. The reason why some people are unable to release themselves of their free-spirited, restless ways, even though they're way past their teenage years, is not because they're born with some unexplainable, unique heroic streak to defy all set conventions, as most of us wish to believe. Whether it's a troubled childhood that they cannot get out of their systems, or some genetic mental disorder, or both that causes these people to be enslaved to their uncontrollable desire to be set free, the bottom line is, they are nowhere closer to freedom than the rest. As the majority of the human population is chained to social norms, so are the free-spirited minds of this world to defying these norms. The romantic notion of ultimate freedom is beyond our reach; regardless of the path we take.

Two months later, I woke up and realised that I did not want him around any longer. I felt that I had finally outlived my fantasy. I no longer saw him as the mysterious sailor who was capable of giving me multiple orgasms but an average guy with smelly feet. A day later he told me that he had to go back to Ayvalik to sort out some stuff and I didn't ask him when and if he was ever coming back. And then he left. The following week I took a flight back to Rome and went back to my usual life, as if nothing had happened. Like I had taken a nice long vacation and now I was back to my usual routine. The only thing that had changed was that I had stopped fantasizing about him. Actually, I preferred not to think about him or our affair. I probably didn't want to question myself as to why I had made such a big deal out of him in the first place. He did call me though, a few months later when he was drunk, as usual, when I had just started hanging out with the Dreamer, and he told me that he really valued the time we had spent together. He had left knowing that we were never meant to be, that we were from two separate worlds. He also told me that he was never going to forget what we had had together till the day he died.

He then said, 'It's very difficult for me to go back to my old ways with women now, to start hanging out with the same kind of women I used to hang out with before I was with you. But it's also impossible for me to be with someone like you again. A girl from your background would never be interested in a guy like me. No, I don't think that will ever happen again.'

2

The Dreamer

Istanbul…the city where east meets west, is a sentence you will hear too often in your lifetime, especially if you're a Turk. My Father hadn't been too keen on the idea of me moving to Istanbul by myself and leaving the comforts of my family home in Rome.

'But Father, what's the point of me starting a university degree here in Rome when your post is about to come to an end in two years? It would only be wiser for me to start university in Istanbul. Then at least I wouldn't have to deal with adjusting myself to a new environment all over again.'

He gave me a doubtful look and then responded, 'But how will you manage on your own? I don't think it's appropriate for a girl of your age to be left on her own.'

I gave a glance at my Mother. At that point she stepped in and said, 'Come on, times have changed.'

I continued without making eye contact with either of them and said, 'Take this summer for example, I was there on my own after you returned to Rome and I think I did pretty well, wouldn't you agree?'

Then I looked up at them while smiling nervously.

My Father stared into my eyes for a moment and then said, 'You better not let me down on this one, or else you'll be sorry.'

I nodded frantically before responding to him, 'I promise, I won't.'

I had lived in Istanbul with my parents for a year prior to that, yet it felt like I was living there for the very first time, ready to experience a very different Istanbul than I had previously done. I was like a prisoner, who after years of being locked away was finally able to see the light of day. Boy, did I exploit freedom to its limits. I was like a greedy kid, trying out every single flavoured candy to the point that it made me want to throw up. To be honest with you, I wasn't really enjoying my freedom; I was just abusing it. Endless drunken nights where I would wake up totally unaware what day of the week or what time of the day I was in. I was like a chameleon, able to transform myself into whatever I was required to be, depending on what I felt like doing on a particular day. On a Monday I would be at a meeting of an underground communist party surrounded by my Turkish and Kurdish comrades, wearing secondhand army boots, jeans and a Che Guevara T-shirt, while smoking excessively on my Maltepe[8] brand cigarettes, raising my left fist high up in the air, screaming out 'Long Live Communism' like a lunatic only to wake up the next day with a sore throat, being unable to speak properly to my Mother who would ring me anxiously from our home in Rome to find out how I was adjusting to my new-found freedom. On a Wednesday I would be in front of my doorstep, dressed from head to toe in black, greeting people who'd showed up at my flat for a session

8 It's one of the cheapest and oldest brands of Turkish cigarettes that's consumed by the majority of the Turkish working class.

on the ouija board. Then on a Thursday, I would be out in Beyoglu,[9] with a group of unfashionably dressed intellectuals, getting trashed in some run-down Meyhane, while passionately discussing the cultural and artistic deficiencies of Turkey as all Turkish intellectuals do. Whereas on a Friday, I would be dancing the night away, with a Marlboro Light in one hand and a glass of Ballantine's whisky in the other, dressed in a skimpy black cocktail dress, rubbing shoulders with the privileged minority at Samdan[10].

I was meant to start attending a graduate course in English Literature at the University of Istanbul in September that year. I use the word 'meant' because I never really turned up more than three times. Given this, you may wonder what the whole point of me being in Istanbul was in the first place. At that stage in my life I was not concerned with developing myself in any way. I had no direction in life whatsoever. The reason I had moved to Istanbul from the picturesque city of Rome, where my family home was then situated, was to get away from my Father. The man who I loved so passionately, maybe too passionately, definitely more than he had deserved to be loved and adored by a daughter, who after years of psychological torment was in fact emotionally crumbling up inside. By then my Father, a high-flying diplomat who I had looked up to with

9 Beyoglu is a European district in Istanbul built in the 1800s during the late Ottoman era, located on the north side of the Golden Horn. It's famous for its rich variety of restaurants, meyhanes, nightclubs and bars. Beyoglu is trendy, bohemian chic yet also a bit rough around the edges. It's the part of the town that never goes to sleep.

10 Samdan is probably as close as you can get to the private club Annabel's in London. Unlike all the other disposable nightclubs that appear only to disappear after a year has gone by, Samdan is still able to attract the elite minority of Istanbul year after year.

great admiration ever since I knew myself, had stripped off, layer by layer, any sense of self-confidence and self-pride I had left in myself. I was in Istanbul to recover my powers, to regain my sanity and to get a chance to find the real me, for until then I had only been able to see myself through his condemning lenses. Yet, although I was able to escape from him physically, I was unable to do so mentally.

Occasionally I would find myself in my parents' three-bedroom flat in Bebek[11], with my new companion, a cat called Jerzy, that I had named after Jerzy Kosinski while reading his novel *The Painted Bird*. I had found him one day wandering aimlessly on the pavement of a side street. He was a handsome tabby with long hair and large strikingly beautiful almond-shaped green eyes. My Uncle had once remarked that his eyes resembled that of the Turkish pop singer Tarkan[12]. The furry little creature had become my favourite companion overnight as I felt we had so much in common. We were both loners and depended on each other for survival. *He* had been abandoned by his Mother and left all on his own to face the polluted, mean streets of Istanbul. I, on the other hand, had made the decision to escape from my family yet was aware somewhere in the back of my mind that I only did so because I had to, not really through choice. For some reason I was always scared at night,

11 I'm not just saying this because we have a flat there, but Bebek is really and truly one of the most beautiful districts in Istanbul. It's a bay that runs along the European shores of the Bosphorus with yachts, fish restaurants and cafés. You can literally smell the sea from your own balcony.

12 Tarkan is the top-selling male superstar in Turkey right now. He is also the first Turkish singer to reach the European and Latin American music charts. Yet more importantly, the man can shake his hips better than a female belly dancer, which has naturally raised a few questions about his sexuality.

but was never quite sure why. Having Jerzy by my side gave me a sense of security. I would hug my cat for moral support, sometimes so tight that he would wriggle away from me and run off to another room. I would usually avoid thinking of the many hurtful events that took place between my Father and I, but some evenings I would lose my strength of mind and start to re-live them one by one, crying with the same desperation as when they actually occurred. But, although he had caused me so much pain I never felt any hatred towards him. He was my idol. Sometimes I would meet a random guy at a bar, invite him over for a drink, and brag about my Father the whole night long. Yes, not only was he an intellectual, an art lover, a man who had comprehensive knowledge on just about anything from Kant's philosophy on aesthetics to the iconography of Michelangelo's ceiling in the Sistine Chapel, but during his university years he used to be the leading vocalist in a rock'n' roll band; he was so cool and I was so proud of him.

So there I was, living in a flat in Istanbul with a cat named Jerzy, after having a crazy affair with a sailor, spending days and nights trying endlessly to find myself, when I came into contact with the Dreamer. I met the Dreamer through another friend, having asked him if he knew anyone who could supply me with some spliff. He told me that he knew a friend who smoked spliffs occasionally and who also lived very close to me, which was very convenient. The Dreamer turned up on my doorstep around nine o'clock one evening. He wasn't a drug dealer, nor was I a dopehead so we had a few moments of awkwardness when we came face to face. I said, 'Hi, you must be…'

'Yes, hi there. How are you?'

'Fine, thanks. So...'

'Yes, so... I live quite close by,' he pointed out.

'Oh, really? Whereabouts is your place?'

'Just across from the Bebek Mosque.'

'So, you're friends with...'

'Yes, we were at the same class at high school. You've known him for a while?'

'Just for a couple of months,' I responded.

Then we looked and smiled nervously at each other. After a few seconds of silence he said, 'He told me that you wanted some...'

'Yes, just for the purpose of experimentation and plus I'm bored out of my brains.'

'You have a cat.'

Jerzy was crawling up my legs.

'Yes, his name is Jerzy. Say hi to our guest, Jerzy.'

Jerzy just stared at my face and then let out a big meow. We both giggled.

'Why don't you come inside? If you like, we can smoke it together,' I suggested as I smiled and lifted my eyebrows. 'Well, that is if you don't have anything more stimulating to do tonight,' I added, just to make sure that I wasn't coming across as being too desperate for company.

'Okay, thanks,' he replied unconfidently as he gazed downwards.

He was a nineteen-year-old, medium height, slim guy with narrow shoulders, long, wavy dark-brown hair, a crooked nose and large dark-brown eyes with extremely long eyelashes. He definitely had a feminine and fragile look about him. Like all rock music lovers that resided in Turkey at that time, he was always dressed in a pair of Levi's 501 jeans and a T-shirt that had the logo of his favourite band. He came from a well-educated middle-class family. His grandfather had served as the mayor of Istanbul in the past and he was living away from his parents who were based in the city of Eskisehir. He had graduated from the reputable Robert College High School a year ago and was not really doing anything, so we had some common ground. More importantly, once we had our very first spliff together, I realised how similar we were in another respect: we both had an endless capacity to create an imaginative world, full of ridiculous yet hilarious scenarios that would spill out of us uncontrollably after merely a few puffs. That night after smoking our very first spliff, we found ourselves in an imaginative courtroom, surrounded by a judge, security guards and the general public. Yes, I had taken Jerzy to court for behavioural misconduct. I was on a stand addressing the court and answering the questions asked by a lawyer, who was of course the Dreamer. My complaint was that although I had taken Jerzy under my wing and out of the filthy streets of Istanbul, through time he had become abusive and impossible to live with. He needed to be sorted out. The lawyer was asking me all sorts of questions. Had I been attentive enough with Jerzy? Was I feeding him on a regular basis? Maybe Jerzy had a history of mental disorder in his family that I wasn't aware of and therefore he was in need of therapy? While all this was going on, Jerzy woke up from his deep sleep, jumped off the couch and was making his way to his favourite spot in the flat, the kitchen, when I picked him up from the floor and forcefully placed him back on the couch.

'No, Jerzy, you cannot leave this courtroom. Do you really want to get into more trouble?'

After that memorable night the Dreamer and I started living together. We weren't lovers but two lost souls who were too weak to face the real world and who could escape from it to some extent through each other's company. We set up a tent in my living room and would spend most of our days and nights inside there, either smoking spliffs and drinking beer, or just sleeping. When I asked him for the second time what he was intending to do with his life, with all seriousness he explained to me that he was in the process of writing a book.

'About what?' I enthusiastically asked.

'Well, it's quite a long story.'

'I don't know if you've noticed but time isn't really an issue for me these days.'

'Do you know the band Queen?'

'Sure.'

'Freddie Mercury is like my God.'

'Didn't he die like two years ago?'

'Yes,' he said as he gazed into the distance. 'When he died I took the first plane to London and slept in front of his house in Earls Court for days. It was an amazing experience. There were hundreds and hundreds of people just like me, who had travelled from different parts of the planet to pay their tribute to him. I know that this may well sound like a load of nonsense to you...'

'No, don't say that. I'm open-minded. If Freddie Mercury is your God then Freddie Mercury is your God. It's actually inspiring to come across someone who's as passionate about something as you are. Like I haven't a clue who my God is. Maybe it's Jerzy?' I thought for a second or two and then continued, 'No, not even him.'

He went on to explain to me how he had met one of the key managers of Queen, a woman called Julia, during one of his trips to London a few years ago. Julia, who was now managing the Queen fan club amongst other things, had worked with Freddie Mercury, Brian May and the rest of the crew since the early seventies. Julia actually had a brief affair with Freddie, in the early seventies, just before he and the rest of the world had realised that in fact he was gay, and had been in love with him secretively ever since. Although she was now a rich woman in her forties, living a privileged and luxurious life through her success with the band, she had devoted her life to keeping the memory of Freddie alive after his much publicized death from Aids. I would listen for hours on end about how the Dreamer first met her and how they eventually became great friends. He would not spare me any details, which helped me visualize vividly in my mind the way she was as a person and the type of life she led. He had shown her a draft of his book that was based on Queen and more specifically on Freddie when he had visited London a few months ago, and she was thrilled and waiting eagerly for him to finish it, but he was taking his time; he wanted it to be perfect. Could I possibly read what he had written so far? He said that maybe I could in the future but he was not yet ready to show it to a third party, it was way too personal for him. He would sometimes go over to his own flat to fetch a few things and on his return tell me that he had spoken to Julia. I would ask him anxiously, 'Did you tell her about me?' to which he would reply, 'Yes, she's really curious about you. She wants us to go to London to visit her. Actually, she even suggested that we should move out there. I think London would do us good. Just think about it. We're just wasting time here.'

That same day we both decided that we had to move to London. We could consider ourselves very lucky as we had Julia on our side who was willing to support us in every possible way. He was going to finish off his book there and I was going to start studying Television Design and Production. It couldn't be more perfect. As there was slightly less than two years left before my parents were returning to Istanbul for good, I was relieved that I had come up with yet another plan that would enable me to find freedom somewhere else, away from my Father. The idea that I would have to live in the same city let alone under the same roof as my Father ever again, made my heart race, causing the effect of an instant yet mild panic attack. No, that could never and should never be an option.

Months passed very quickly as we were constantly stoned, making plans for our future life together with Julia in London. You see, because Julia had been in love with Freddie since her teenage years, she never was able to have a family of her own. Sometimes she would have short flings but nobody could replace Freddie. Yet her longing to have children was to be eventually satisfied to a certain degree as she was prepared to become our guardian angel in a matter of months. We even talked about broadening our family unit by adopting a child around the time he became an acclaimed author and I was working behind the scenes of a well-known Television Network. Yet we would sometimes find it difficult to decide what would happen to our beloved kid if either of us fell in love with someone else as we weren't a couple but just really good friends. Maybe we had to rethink the adoption, but we had a long life ahead of us to do so.

Three months later I was in my flat getting myself prepared to leave for London the following day just after spending the summer with my parents in Italy. I had spent the whole of the three months there, using every trick in the book to persuade my Father to send me to London. The only downside to the happy ending was that I had been forced to find a second home for Jerzy when I got back to Istanbul. As I placed a picture of him into one of my suitcases I sighed and then said out loud,

'You'll always have a special place in my heart.'

No, it wasn't going to be all that easy to put his memory behind me. Especially when taking into account that I had a bust portrait of Jerzy tattooed on my right shoulder. Suddenly I went back to the moment when I had left him in the living room of his new home. Just as I was leaving, I had knelt down and whispered in his ear,

'I'm sorry for having to leave you like this. I'm going to miss you like hell you little, precious, innocent boy. You've been such a great support. Baby, please forgive me for letting you down like this. If it wasn't for London I would've never left you. Your new owner, she's a good woman. Maybe she's a bit of a nymphomaniac but at least instead of getting stoned with me and the Dreamer you'll get a chance to socialize a bit. I hope you'll have a wonderful life. You deserve it more than any cat I know.'

Then the doorbell rang. It was the Dreamer. I left what I was doing, went to the door and opened it unwillingly. We had spoken on the phone the night before and I had told him that yes, I was going to London but I wanted to do it on my own. I always felt stronger and more capable on my own, men for some reason made me feel weak and vulnerable. I guess it was a father thing. All our fantasies about our future life together with Julia were fine but it had just dawned on me that it was a bit ridiculous to plan a future with a guy who wasn't my boy-friend and a woman I had never come into contact with. As he entered the living room and sat down on the couch he quickly grabbed a cigarette from his ruck-sack and lit it up nervously. His hands were shaking and he kept staring at the floor as he started to explain himself to me. He said,

'The truth is, I am in love with you.'

'What?' I yelled out loud as I sprung from my seat. 'I thought that you were gay.'

He looked up and said, 'What makes you think that?'

'Remember? Freddie Mercury is your God. And what about the dream you had, where you were having a bubble bath with Freddie while he was rubbing soap all over you? Isn't that gay enough?'

'That was just a dream. Freddie Mercury is my God, but you're the one I am in love with. You are the most amazing girl I have ever met. I cannot survive without you. You mean everything to me. You are my best friend, my Mother, the girl I love. Please don't leave me.'

And then he started sobbing. Unfortunately his feelings weren't mutual. All I could think of was that I wished he would leave soon without making a big scene as I had limited time to pack. I told him that he had to leave and I would call him from London. He looked into my eyes desperately and I knew that I was being way too cruel towards him but I just couldn't help it and then, knowing he had to, he left.

A distant friend of the family, a Turkish girl in her early thirties who had been working as a nanny for the past four years in London came to Heathrow Airport to pick me up. I was to stay with her in Chelsea until I found a place of my own. After leaving my stuff in her flat I went to my new school to register on a foundation course on Television Design and Production. It was all very new and exciting. The Nanny was naturally very friendly and supportive towards me in the beginning. I was sleeping in the living room of her one bedroom flat which was in fact the attic of a rundown Victorian house. The owner of the house was an old English widow who lived with her handsome, public school, thirty-something son below us and who always kept forgetting my name. Unfortunately we had to share the only bathroom in the house with them. Whenever I took a bath, I would perform with utter disgust the same ritual of scraping off the dirt from the bathtub, a mixture of soap and dead skin that had turned into some sort of solid second coat that covered the bathtub from head to toe. Then I would fill the bathtub with hot water and did I forget to mention that there was no shower? Yes, as most foreigners do when they arrive in the UK, I was trying to adjust to the impracticalities of the lifestyle here in the best possible way.

Barely two weeks had passed, when I started to notice that the Nanny, who had been all friendly and comforting towards me, was making it obvious, although I was paying half of the rent, that she didn't want me around any longer. I realised that I was making her feel insecure. There I was, a fresh-looking nineteen-year-old girl, who had come to London to start a new life and there she was, an overweight woman in her early thirties who, after getting her university degree in Istanbul, had decided to come to London to develop her English while she worked as a part-time nanny, hoping that London had more to offer her. Yet it hadn't. After all that time spent here she was miserably single and still a nanny. I knew that her growing dislike towards me wasn't personal, I simply reminded her of her own failure. Nonetheless, to be honest with you, living with somebody for the first time in a foreign country who basically didn't want me around made me feel vulnerable and lonely, so I called the Dreamer to tell him that I missed him and had changed my mind and that he should come to London as soon as possible.

As we met up ten days later at Victoria station, I was relieved to see him as after leaving the Nanny's flat a few days before, I had moved into the flat of a Polish student who was doing the same course as me. We had started chatting at breaks and he had kindly offered to share his one-bedroom flat in Hampstead with me when I had told him that I was desperately looking for a place to stay. He was a tall, well-built young man in his late twenties, with porcelain white skin and short pitch-black hair. He was quite good looking in fact but there was something rather strange about him, which I could not really pin down. I would find out the hard way once I moved in with him. He was all very nice to me the first night and even offered to sleep on the couch while I took over his entire bedroom. When I woke up the following morning, I found him having a lengthy discussion with himself, which did seem a bit odd. Well, I occasionally talk to myself out loud as well but I usually only say a few words or one or two sentences; it never turns into a serious discussion. I said, 'Good morning,' and he lifted his head up and stared at me as if he had seen me for the very first time.

He looked rough and disorientated. Maybe the couch was too uncomfortable to sleep on or maybe he had spent the whole night fantasizing and masturbating about the girl sleeping in his bedroom? But I somehow felt that it was more than that. Then he took out his notebook, showed me the notes he'd been taking in class and as we were discussing the assignments that we had been given he kept going on and on about how stressed he was. As he expressed his worries his voice became louder and louder to the point that he was shouting like a mad man. Believe me, it was scary. After he gradually calmed down, I told him that a friend of mine was coming over from Turkey and it was impossible for the two of us to stay here with him. Did he know of anyone who rented out rooms? He asked me immediately, 'Is your friend a guy?' to which I replied, 'Yes.'

I could tell from the disillusioned expression on his face that my answer had disappointed him. He said, 'My Mother has this lady friend, an old Polish lady who lives by herself in a small flat in Islington. She sometimes rents out a room. I can ask her if you like.'

The Old Polish Lady knew him through his Mother who owned an exclusive brothel in Warsaw, and explained to me later on that he had been verbally and physically abused by his Mother from a very early age. When she first came into contact with him he was a beautiful boy around the age of seven or eight. He must have taken after his Mother who was also a stunning woman in her youth. Nevertheless, she would constantly yell at her illegitimate son, smacking, hitting and even punching him as hard as she could, whenever she could. I assume that, like me, he had come to London to get away from his abusive parent, yet for him it was too late. He had been clinically diagnosed as a schizophrenic for some time now and wasn't fit to work or even attend school. He dropped out of the course a month later.

As we unpacked and settled into our new home, which was a large single room consisting of a wall-to-wall built-in wardrobe, a chest of drawers and a single bed, I finally was able to take a deep breath. I had told the Dreamer that the only way we could stay together in a single room was that he would need to sleep on the floor while I slept in the bed, to which he had agreed submissively. He also agreed to other terms, like he had to wait in the corridor every time I got dressed and had to disappear for two to three hours at least whenever I needed to study. We would usually spend evenings in our room as he would go on and on about Julia; how she was promoting a new band in the States but hopefully would be joining us in a few months. Then at around midnight, when the Old Polish Lady was fast asleep in her bedroom just right next to our one, we would sneak quietly into the kitchen, open the fridge and steal small portions of her food. Sometimes it would be just a plate of some Polish dish she had prepared or two slices of bread and some cheese. As I was financially taking care of all the Dreamer's expenses in addition to my own, with the money my Father was sending on a monthly basis, our meals usually consisted of rice with ketchup and sometimes a bar of Snickers. Of course, the Dreamer could always ask for Julia's financial support, but wouldn't it be better if we could put up with our current situation a little bit longer until she returned from California? We didn't want her to get the wrong idea that we were trying to take advantage of her in any way. The Old Polish Lady would see us digging into our not so appealing plates full of rice and ketchup and would usually offer us what she had cooked for the day, which we would accept, but this still did not stop us from going back to the kitchen in the middle of the night and stealing her food. I reckon we were doing it purely for the thrill of it. Then we would hide the food inside our jumpers, and we would tiptoe back to our room while giggling along the way. It was always his idea. I guess he knew that my guilty conscience would prevent me from becoming any closer to her. On rare occasions we would join her in the living room and exchange a few sentences with her, yet we would retire to our bedroom soon after and do our own thing. The Dreamer always had something negative to say about her even though she was so nice and hospitable to the two weird and not so friendly strangers that were renting a room in her flat. He was afraid that I would become friends with her and he never really wanted to share me with anyone.

After a few months had gone by, our relationship, friendship or whatever the hell it was that we were having was going downhill. The only time I was actually nice to him was when he was telling me his amazing stories, but even with that I was starting to show signs of disinterest. He usually would be stuck in the corridor, in front of our room, begging me to let him in, after he had tried to kill some time by taking long walks for two to three hours in order to let me study. He would whisper desperately, 'Come on you have to let me in, I cannot wander around in the streets any longer. It's cold out there you know, please let me in,' to which I would usually reply by shouting back at him, telling him that I still had more work to do, that he should find something else to do with his spare time and that it wasn't my problem.

And sometimes when I did let him back in after five hours or so, I would explain to him that it would be better if he went back to Turkey and that I had had enough of looking after him. At this stage he would start crying and beg me to rethink.

'You're just saying that because you're frustrated. It's only natural. You've been locked up studying in your room all day. I think you need to get some fresh air. Hey, why don't we go out for a drink?'

'I am frustrated all right. Frustrated at having to see your miserable face each day. Why don't you get it? I want you out of my life! You're suffocating me!'

'No, no, please just listen to me. Okay, I'll leave. If you don't want me in three days' time I promise you, I'll leave.'

By then he had become well accustomed to my abusive ways and had learnt how to deal with me. He was aware that three days was long enough for me to calm down and even forget that I had asked him to leave in the first place. I guess the reason I was so cruel to him was that I didn't love him or really care for him. And he was still there with me just because it was so hard to get rid of him and sometimes it felt comforting to come back from school to somebody, a companion of some sort. Yet his tourist visa was to run out soon so he had to leave and go back to Istanbul to extend it.

Once he was gone I started to spend more and more time with the Old Polish Lady. I would usually join her in her living room and we'd watch *EastEnders* together. As each day passed, little by little we found out more about each other's life and felt more comfortable in one another's company. I even looked forward to coming home each day from school to chat with her and tell her how my day had been. For the first time in my life I felt safe and at home in this cramped little flat in Islington.

Then one day she asked me what on earth I was doing with the Dreamer. She said that he was a parasite, a loser who had no direction in life. She gave me an unbelieving look when I told her that in fact he was in the process of writing a book. And after the words came out of my mouth I admitted to myself something I already knew, but had avoided for a long time, that actually, all that he was doing was making up stories to the extent that he was convinced that they were true. It had been a purely convenient coincidence for our paths to cross in the first place. I was unhappy as hell when I first met him and was looking desperately for some escape route to help me forget how miserable I was, and he was generous enough to share his rich fantasy world with me. Finally I had reached a point where I was confident enough to experience London without having to rely on his imagination. Nevertheless I had to know the truth for sure so the following day I called the Queen Fan

Club and asked to be put through to Julia. To my surprise a woman by the name of Julia in the Queen Fan Club did really exist. Yet when I mentioned the Dreamer to her, this young Turkish boy that she had befriended three years ago who was in the process of writing a book that she was so keen to publish, she told me that she had no idea what the hell I was going on about. I was curious to find out how far he had actually gone, so I asked, hadn't she had a love affair with Freddie when she was young and wasn't she still infatuated with him? She replied in a repulsed manner, 'I am happily married and have been so for the past thirty-two years.'

After apologizing for disturbing her with my strange questions I hung up. I also felt repelled, yet saddened at the same time. It was terrible that he had been lying to me all along, but what he had been doing to himself was actually worse. After all, it hadn't only been me that he was lying to. He had been lying to all of his friends, as well as anyone he came into close contact with. But why would someone do something like that? That night when he called me from Istanbul, I confronted him. I really didn't want to but I believed that for his sake I should. Maybe for once I would be of use to him, help him to wake up from his dream, enable him to switch back to the real world from this fantasy world he had created so convincingly. He denied all my allegations and said that I had spoken to the wrong Julia; the real one was in California, producing an album with a new band. Then a few days later his Mother called me. She told me that her son had been telling the truth all along. I guess he probably had threatened her with suicide or something and maybe, just as she was on the phone with me, he was dangling his feet out of the window just to make sure that she would go ahead with his story. I felt sorry for her, as it must be terribly hard for a Mother to have to deal with something like that. I told her that I appreciated her call, but Julia or no Julia, the time had come for us to go our separate ways. He tried to contact me on a few other occasions but the Old Polish Lady would always answer the phone and tell him that he had to stop bothering me.

To this day, I sometimes think of him, especially when I come across anything related to Queen or Freddie Mercury and wonder what he's up to, if he was ever able to come to terms with his illness and accept life in the real world, appreciate in any way what it has to offer.

3

The Proofreader

It was mid-September, and a year had passed since I arrived in London. I had just started the first year of a bachelor's degree in Television Design and Production, after finishing the foundation course the previous year. I can't say that I was enjoying it immensely but I knew I could not afford to change my mind again. Yet I also knew that if given the chance I would; I could have studied Acting or Fine Arts instead, Television Design and Production was a bit too uncreative and uninspiring. However, I had to go ahead with it and for once in my life finish off something I had started. I wasn't getting the highest grades in the class but so far I was above average, which for me was a huge success. I don't know why I had been such a failure at school until then; maybe it was all down to my stubborn streak. Regardless of the tremendous pressure and mistreatment I had received over the years from my Father to succeed at school, I still kept on failing. What he did or said made no difference; I still would get the worst grades. It drove him insane. Maybe it was the only way I could show him some form of a reaction, as I never had the right to have an opinion or a say on anything.

Being the new kid on the block didn't help either. I always felt out of place at school and for most of the time I was in my own little world. Although I was there physically, in my mind I was miles away. It was as if there was a semi-transparent shield over my head that would blind my receptiveness to what was happening around me. When people spoke, for most of the time I wouldn't hear words or sentences but just some deep indecipherable murmur. I felt that I was surrounded by a fusion of colours and forms; often being unable to set buildings, trees and people apart from one another. The shield would appear as soon as I was forced to interact with people or situations that for one reason or another intimidated me. It was there when my Father was around, when I was at school, or among a new crowd of people. It was my safety blanket. Whenever I had to let it down, I felt nauseous, cold and agitated. Like my Mother, the shield made me feel warm and safe. I remember how the other kids would give me this strange look when I would cling on to my Mother's waist and refuse to let go, and she would literally have to push me away, minutes after the school bell had gone off, trying to reassure me that in fact this was for my own good.

Like all the other kids I had to prepare myself for life. Nevertheless, I would sit for a whole day in class without listening to a single word. There was really no point in me being there. Sometimes I would promise myself that I was going to concentrate and listen to what the teacher was mumbling about, yet this would never last for more than a few minutes and before I knew it I would be in my own fantasy world again, either giving an earthshaking live concert to a massive audience, doing cool karate moves to some kid that was picking on me at school, or becoming invisible and then going out for a shopping spree without having to spend a single penny. I was only able to remove the semi-transparent shield that had been my companion throughout childhood after I moved to London. It didn't happen overnight, but little by little I found the confidence to interact with people, and once I got a taste for it I realised that I didn't want to be an outsider any longer. Yet, to this day it occasionally resurfaces but at least it's no longer a part of my everyday life.

By now, I had become best friends with the Old Polish Lady. We would cook meals for each other, and spend evenings revealing our most intimate secrets to one another. Now and again I would have this recurring dream about Jerzy. I would be walking aimlessly in Istanbul and all of a sudden I would bump into him by mere coincidence. At first he would tell me that he had missed me a lot and that he was so glad to see me. But then there would be a sudden change in his pleasant tone of voice, and he would start questioning why I had turned my back on him and left him on his own out there. 'Don't you love me anymore?' he would ask with an innocent little boy's voice.

I would try to explain to him that I couldn't possibly have brought him over to London. How was he to survive the six months' quarantine? Yet I found it difficult convincing myself, let alone him. I'd wake up from the dream on a terrible guilt trip, then join the Old Polish Lady in her living room and cry my eyes out to her. She probably thought that I was mad, crying like that over a cat, but at least she was there to listen and tried in her own way to put me at ease.

I would also talk to her about my boyfriends and even go into lengthy details about my sexual experiences. She would confide in me as well, about her two unsuccessful attempts at marriage and the affair she had had, right after her second marriage, with the man of her life, a rich, handsome, Polish businessman. Although they fell madly in love and he wanted to marry her, the affair had to end due to his persistence to only have anal sex with her. She would say, 'If it was only a few times a month I could possibly compromise as that's what relationships are all about, but that was all he ever wanted.'

For years she had questioned herself on whether or not she had made the right decision, to turn down the love of her life purely because of his sexual preference. Nevertheless, she told me with all frankness that she realised that she had made the right choice when she went to visit him and his new wife in their lavish new home just outside Warsaw, many years after, and was disgusted to find a washbowl full of cloths covered in shit, hidden somewhere in the bathroom. But of course if she *had* married him she would be living in a villa in Konstancin instead of a small modest flat in Islington, overlooking McDonald's.

She would often advise me to use my brain and good looks in order to find the ideal rich husband. Life was too difficult and too short to be fooling around; I had to be wise and think of securing my future. I told her that I was, and was studying for that reason. But why study so hard and work so hard when you can gain a privileged life off someone else's back? There was no such thing as true love; if I was smart enough I would marry a rich man just for his money, regardless of whether I was in love or not. Even if you did find love it was never going to last forever. It was pointless. Although we were inseparable, I still knew that we also were miles apart in terms of how we perceived life. I also couldn't help but question the reason why she had not done so herself. At the end of the day, she was the one who had turned her back on a fortune literally to save her own ass.

Yet, she was still able to convince me to go on a few dates with this rich Polish guy in his mid-forties that was a friend of hers. He owned a big publishing house in London. There was nothing majorly wrong with the guy apart from the fact that he had a massive crooked nose, a tiny weenie chin, and a wide forehead. What's more, he was a sleazebag. Ugly and sleazy; never a good combination. Nevertheless, like all sleazebags, he was mesmerized by me from the moment he laid eyes on me and tried ever so hard to impress me. Now and again he would send me a bouquet of roses; or better, the best chef in town to prepare me some sushi. The Old Polish Lady was definitely more thrilled about his interest in me than I was.

'What if he asks you to marry him?' she would say and, totally disregarding the obvious look of disinterest in my face, would continue, 'Could you imagine? He would throw a big wedding for you and you would be on the front cover of all the Polish newspapers!'

'Yes, as the idiot, greedy gold-digger who married the ugly womanizer,' I would say to myself.

Then finally realising my lack of enthusiasm for the whole scenario she would say, 'Come on, at least he's wealthy; you'll have a comfortable life.'

Actually, if he ever got his sleaziness under control, which rarely happened, he was a good guy deep down inside. Men like that are so used to rejection that it really takes a serious effort on your part to make them fully aware that you simply are not interested. You can tell it to their face but they will still try to put their tongue down your throat at the end of the night, just before they drop you home. So, I have no clue as to what I was thinking when he suggested that we go for a drink at his place one night after dinner. I guess sometimes I just go with the flow.

That night, I remember that I was wearing my favourite pale blue Versace cocktail dress for the occasion. As soon as we went into his large, two bedroom apartment in St John's Wood that looked more like a hotel suite with its synchronized furniture than someone's home, he went straight to the bar in the living room to pour us some champagne. Then as we both were holding onto our icy cold champagne glasses he gave me a tour of his flat, and we stopped for longer than was required in his bedroom. As we were standing awkwardly next to his bed, I suddenly noticed a squeezed tube of KY Jelly by his bedside. 'Why on earth was it there?' I wondered. Did he use it for masturbation or to fuck prostitutes up their asses? You just don't leave a KY Jelly out in the open; it's almost as shameful as leaving out your dirty knickers inside out. There was a beautiful navy silk kimono lying on his bed. I asked him if he had got it on one of his trips to Japan. He said that it was a present from a Japanese client. Then I asked him if he had some Frank Sinatra as I slowly made my way back to his living room and placed myself down on one of the sofas. He didn't, but he put on Jazz FM instead. As I gazed around his living room I told him that he could have made a better effort in decorating his flat, to which he replied,

'I am a busy man, it needs a woman's touch.' Then he said,

'I want to get into something more comfortable; I'll be back in a minute.'

And in less than a minute he was back wearing his beautiful navy kimono, with nothing underneath. He sat next to me on the sofa and said, 'You are a very beautiful, attractive girl, you turn me on a lot.'

You know, when you know exactly what is going on but are too scared to look? Well, I was having that moment. I knew that he was touching himself but I didn't dare look. 'Maybe I should leave,' I thought to myself. All of a sudden he got up and stood in front of me, while holding his large erect penis in his hand and said,

'Imagine me being inside of you. How I'd love to fuck you hard!'

'How interesting,' I replied with a dull expression on my face while I took another drag from my cigarette followed by a sip of champagne and looked the other way. Before I knew it he was giving himself a hand job right in front of my face.

'Are you out of your mind? Come on! You look ridiculous,' I cried out and he told me that it was too late for him to stop; he had to come.

At that moment I pushed him out of my way, got up and went to the far corner of the room and said, 'Okay, that is your problem but don't you dare come any closer to me and don't even think about staining my favourite Versace dress or I'll kill you.'

I know the whole thing sounds disgusting and very awkward, but I found it funny and tried really hard to keep a straight face. After he came I said that I had to leave; the show was over.

One Monday morning I had skipped class in order to go to the Turkish Consulate General in Knightsbridge to renew my passport with a Turkish girlfriend of mine, and I came across the Proofreader. He was standing in front of us in the queue and when his turn came up, the civil servant on the other side of the screen, a guy with a dark complexion and a heavy south-eastern dialect, addressed him by his first name and asked how his proofreading job was going, while holding a burning cigarette in his hand. The Proofreader was a tall, good-looking, forty-five year old man with broad shoulders, greyish hair, dressed in casual yet tasteful clothes. His style was very Indiana Jones, minus the hat. He stood out from the rest of the Turkish male population in the building who were noticeably dark and short. However, it wasn't only that. He had an extremely refined look about him. He didn't look typically Turkish at all but seemed to be more of a man of the world. An intellectual, maybe an art lover, but definitely a man of sophisticated taste and refined pleasures. Someone who could drop by for tea at my parents house one afternoon and have a lengthy discussion with my Father about art, music and politics. At one point he turned his head round to take a brief look at me. Had he found me attractive? Even so, maybe he was married. It would be too embarrassing to introduce myself right there and then. What would I say? I gave it a thought for a few seconds, but couldn't come up with anything plausible that would make any sense to him so I gave up. When we left the Turkish Consulate I spoke only of him to my girlfriend. Wasn't he amazing?

'I'm in love,' I said, in the heat of the moment without really meaning it.

We thought of ways I could possibly meet him.

'Maybe you could call up the Consulate a few days later and ask for his details. You can say that you have some school assignments that need to be proofread?' my girlfriend suggested.

'Yes!' I shouted fervently before giving her a big wet kiss on the cheek. 'Yes, that's definitely a brilliant idea.'

As I said goodbye to my friend and walked into Knightsbridge tube station I thought to myself, why wait for a few days, do it tomorrow, or even better, do it today if I could make it home early enough. As soon as I got home I told the Old Polish Lady that I had seen the man of my dreams. I told her his name and his profession and she looked at me with a pleasant smile on her face and told me that she knew him. She even had his phone number as they had met on a few occasions through a Polish girlfriend of hers that he used to date. At that point I was jumping up and down, bouncing around with excitement. Then I began to belly dance with the most exaggerated movements at which she started laughing with an astonished look on her face. I finally sat down next to her when I was out of breath. She said, 'I don't know if he's seeing someone, but he's definitely not married. He's not the marrying type anyway.'

I begged for her to give me his number, which she did straight away. After exhausting myself by talking about him with her for another hour or so, I went back to my room, lay down on my bed and kept looking at the piece of paper that had his number written on it.

Should I call him tonight? Well, it would be too soon. Maybe it would be wiser to call him tomorrow. Let's also not forget that if I waited too long he could easily forget about the girl who was standing behind him in the queue at the Turkish Consulate. I was aware that by choosing to call a complete stranger, I was acting way too forward, especially for a girl. But since I felt so strongly about him and I had the chance to contact him, I couldn't possibly forget about the whole thing. It would be stupid to do so. The worst scenario would be that he would turn me down, saying he was already involved or something, but who cares if he did? Okay, I would feel embarrassed and disappointed at first, maybe feel slightly depressed for a week and then I would eventually get over it. I definitely wasn't going to be scarred for life by a complete stranger and there was a low possibility that I would ever come across him again in the future, and even if I did he might not even remember me, and even if he did...enough!

I was going to call him, end of story. There was no point in going over and over the ramifications of a single phone call. Why ruin my state of ecstasy over what might happen, while I could embrace it and just enjoy the moment instead? It was simply useless creating scenarios in my mind, as it was impossible to ever know what the future would bring. Even if I thought of every possible consequence that might exist, I knew that I could never get it totally right. The bottom line was, I had already made up my mind and no rational *future* bullshit was ever going to make me change it.

The next day I called him around 3 pm, giving him way too much time to finish his lunch. When he answered his phone after a few rings, I said,

'I hope I am not bothering you and I haven't caught you in the middle of anything?'

As soon as I said it I had this vision of him all sweaty, on top of a faceless woman, pumping away as he went for the phone, but then forced myself to focus on what I was trying to do. He said,

'Yes I'm free to talk, how can I help you?'

He probably thought I was calling him up for some proof-reading job. As I opened my mouth to speak, my heart started racing like crazy and I realised I was blushing as I felt a sudden increase in my body temperature, but it had to be now or never.

I said, 'I know this is going to sound strange and it is strange, but yesterday I saw you in the Turkish Consulate. I was standing behind you with a girlfriend of mine. And, well, I know that what I am doing here is a bit weird but believe me I am not a pervert, well not in the serious sense anyway. I was wondering if you would like to meet up for a coffee or a drink, whatever you prefer, whenever is convenient with you?'

From the tone of his voice I could tell that he was both surprised and flattered and was smiling when he asked me which one of the two girls I was. I explained by giving him a thorough physical description of myself in order to avoid any misunderstandings. We decided to meet up that same week on Thursday evening at 8 pm for a drink at a pub in Hampstead. As I put the phone down I looked at myself in the mirror on the wall that was facing me, and yes indeed, I had turned the colour of a pumpkin. The following day the Old Polish Lady left for Warsaw for a two-week break which was just perfect timing and I waited eagerly for another day to pass.

As I entered the pub, on a Thursday night at five minutes

past eight, I saw him sipping on a glass of red wine by the bar. I was so worried that for some reason I would not recognize him, or that he wouldn't turn up. To be frank with you, I have never been a big fan of pubs, but this particular one was unlike most pubs that you come across in London, that are stuffy and gloomy, and have dirty carpets and smell heavily of a mixture of beer, wine and cigarettes. No, this pub was more like the ones you see outside London, that are polished and clean with immaculately dressed and well-mannered landlords serving people their drinks over the bar. After all, I knew he was a man of refined taste.

As I finally approached him he said, 'Hi, how are you? What would you like to drink?' in a noticeably nervous manner.

I hadn't expected him to be so nervous, as he was a good-looking man who had been asked out on a date by a girl less than half his age, but then on second thoughts, maybe it was natural. After getting me a glass of white wine he suggested that we find a place at one of the tables towards the back. Once we found our spot and sat down, we started chatting uncomfortably. It was kind of awkward looking into his eyes. I felt all shy and giggly inside, though I tried to keep a straight face and to maintain eye contact with him as we spoke.

Sometimes while he was talking I would switch off and imagine what he would actually do if I was to suddenly let out a big stinking fart or, being totally unaware, had a dark greenish snot poking out from one of my nostrils, staring him in the face. Now that would definitely change the pace of things. You see, life is so complex that you are never able to take every little detail into account. I remember a similar case when I was in the last year of high school in Rome and was dating the best looking guy at school. After we had been seeing each other for a fortnight and he was walking me home everyday after school just to spend more time with me, regardless of the fact that it took us an hour to walk all the way, the least and worst expected thing happened. As he was walking me home one day, to my surprise, I suddenly noticed a big yellow snot stretching all the way from his left nostril right across his cheek. If it was now, I might have got over the whole thing, but when you are a teenager you find it very hard to come to terms with the fact that the guy who you regard as the personification of coolness is also possessed with a body that will produce an excessive amount of farts, piss, snot and shit, throughout his life. I guess it's also a bit of Turkish thing; us Turks are conditioned from a very early age, by our parents and the ones closest to us, to be fully alert at all times regarding bodily fluids and their urges to resurface. But the undeniable tragic truth is that I fart a lot and considering the number of sleepless nights spent staring at the ceiling, while a guy is fast asleep right next to me, being worried sick that eventually I will fall asleep as well and the poor guy will wake up with the loud sound of my fart which would frighten him like some earthshaking thunderbolt in the middle of the night, I obviously take the whole thing a bit too far. And life can be so unpredictable every so often. Like the time I was staying over at this Italian guy's house after going out on a first date with him to the private members' club Tramp in Jermyn Street off Piccadilly, and then smoking a few spliffs at his place later on. I was too stoned to go home so I asked if I could sleep in the spare room. He was cute and we had exchanged a few kisses while smoking but I wanted to take things slow. The next morning I woke up with this terrible stomach ache. I knew at that instant that I had diarrhoea but wasn't aware of the severity of my case until I locked myself in his bathroom. Not only was the whole ceremony so dramatic like some Wagnerian coda, waking the neighbours up as well as him at 8 am on a Sunday morning, but almost half an hour later when I finally found the strength and courage to lift my bum off the toilet seat and head out, I realised that as I opened the bathroom door I allowed the most disgustingly intense smell to quickly make its way into every corner of his flat. When I went home soon after, without saying goodbye, he called me sometime in the afternoon to ask if I was all right. I told him that I was just fine. I was too embarrassed to mention the word diarrhoea so he naturally assumed that it was just me being me and that if he was ever going to start seeing me he needed to get used to me stinking his flat with my loud smelly farts every morning. He never called me again. Thank God that as you get older, you get used to the fact that like you, everybody has a body, which offers an endless variety of farts, snot and shit. And once you are able to get over the initial disgust of someone else's, you find it even comforting in a way that you are not the only one on this planet who is sometimes in danger of fainting from your own stinking fart. Having said all that, I still don't think that it goes down too well on a first date.

As we were into our second glass of wine, the tension between us slowly began to disappear. He told me that he had been living in London for the past twenty-four years. He had come as a student to study guitar, but was never able to complete his studies and after trying his luck in a few odd jobs, had been working as a proofreader for the past twelve years.

'I still regret not finishing my studies. It was my dream to become a professional guitarist but I ran out of money. I had to put my dream aside and focus on making a living. I would've never thought I'd end up being a proofreader but it was the best option at the time. It's funny where life can take you...'

Naturally he had had quite a number of girlfriends but had never been married. Well, if you are forty-five, not in a long-term relationship and have never been married, most people would assume that there must be something seriously wrong with you. Maybe you're secretly gay, but I believe it's more likely that you are for one reason or another scared to commit. You can be secretly gay when you're in your twenties but by the time you hit forty you're more likely to have your priorities sorted out. I really didn't care that there was a high possibility I could fall for this commitment-freak, as I wasn't the most reliable person when it came to relationships; then again I was just twenty. Not only was he single but he was also living with his bedridden Mother who was in the late stages of Alzheimer's disease. Yes, the whole set up was very Anthony Perkins. But I really didn't mind as by this time I was into my fourth glass of white wine, and was considerably drunk. The place was closing up so he offered to drop me home.

When we arrived outside my apartment I said, 'My landlady is away so would you care to come up for one last drink?'

He looked at me, while still seated in front of the wheel trying to figure out what I exactly meant by 'one last drink', and then accepted. As we were sipping our wine, sitting next to one another at the edge of two separate sofas in the living room, I held his hand and he smiled shyly like a fifteen-year-old virgin. Aware of his shyness, he tried to cover it up by leaning forward and kissing me softly, to which I answered back by grabbing onto the collar of his shirt and kissing him more passionately. Then continuing to do so I knelt down in front of him and pulled him down towards me and we began to sink lower and lower until we continued our kissing session lying on the carpet. It was all kind of surreal to have him lying there with me on the flower-patterned carpet of the Old Polish Lady's living room surrounded by plastic flowers, flower-patterned pillows and flower-patterned sofas, with various cheap ornaments placed here and there, and walls adorned with mirrors and reproductions of Monet's waterlilies. Yes, after all, the Old Polish Lady was still a young girl at heart who loved anything that was pink and floral. I cannot recall the exact details of our first sex session as by this time I was totally wasted. All I can remember is the grin on his face as he said goodbye to me before I shut the door. So I assume my performance must have been anything but bad.

I have to admit that I am somewhat more relaxed and innovative if I am to have sex with someone new or someone that I have been with on only a few occasions, if I have had a few drinks. Yet this can be quite tricky because if I go too far and have way too much to drink, I attack my prey with great passion and usually stop in the middle of our lovemaking session to turn my back and fall asleep. This must be quite disappointing for the guy, who at that stage is thanking his sweet Jesus, Moses or Muhammad for being lured into bed by a girl of such enthusiasm.

I thought that he must have been quite surprised that I slept with him on our first date, a fact that he eventually admitted to. Although I can come across as being quite promiscuous, I never like to sleep with complete strangers and I don't favour one-night stands. You see, that night after our lengthy and pleasurable conversation at the pub where I realised that I was still into him as much as the first time I laid eyes on him three days before, I decided that playing hard to get was a pointless waste of our valuable time together. I knew that I liked the way he looked, the way he carried himself, his ideas and the way he spoke; so I was eager to find out if I was going to like the rest. And although I don't remember much of it, I do remember that it felt good, felt right, and that maybe it would feel even better the next time.

Nonetheless, I did once try the 'wait until you know him better so he can respect you' strategy on an Australian guy I met at Eclipse in Walton Street after being heavily brainwashed by my girlfriends. He was a very tall, athletic-looking man (as most Australians are) in his late forties who was from Melbourne and spent the majority of his time in London because of his business. We had chatted for an hour or so at Eclipse before exchanging numbers. After calling me three days later and asking me out, we had met on a number of occasions for drinks, dinner and a movie. Soon, I realised that I was really starting to fancy him. I even began to have fantasies about getting married and moving to Australia with him, which is so unlike me. Although I avoided sleeping with him for six months, every time we met, I felt that we had an extreme chemistry. Not just sexual, but something mental as well. He was very affectionate and even if we never ended up going to his flat by the river and having wild sex, we would walk the streets of Chelsea, holding hands, cuddling and kissing continuously. Of course, his regular trips back to Melbourne also helped in postponing the inevitable.

Then came the big night. I accepted his offer to go back to his place for a drink. By this time I was fully aware that if someone asked you to have a drink at their place, it was possibly a polite way of asking 'Can we fuck?' After we had been on his sofa kissing and fondling each other for at least an hour, he got up and took off his shirt, then his trousers and finally his boxer shorts, and suddenly I was faced with the penis equivalent of Mount Everest. My jaw dropped. I was both shocked and astonished. 'Could something that huge really exist?' I kept asking myself. Although he was a very tall guy, still his huge penis looked as if it ought to be attached to a donkey or a horse rather than a human being. I said, 'I've never seen anything like this before. Let me have a good look at it.' I knelt down in front of him to examine his penis from different angles. 'Wow, it's gigantic. Have you ever considered a career in the porn industry?' He smiled back at me with a doubtful look.

'Come on, I am not trying to embarrass you here. It's a gift. A very, very large gift. God has been mighty generous with you.'

He told me that sometimes it was a problem for him. Then he suggested that we continue our lovemaking session in his bedroom. I took the half-empty bottle of Johnnie Walker Red Label with me, in case I needed some extra help, as I made my way to his bedroom. I kept telling myself, 'Who knows?

Maybe I have an extremely wide and deep vagina, but just don't know it yet.'

Who was I really kidding? By that time I had slept with enough guys to know what my vagina was capable of. And tragically, when his penis was merely halfway inside of me, my eyes ready to explode from their sockets, I pushed him away as it was just physically impossible to have intercourse with him. He didn't insist as he must have been quite used to such a reaction, but it was really frustrating being unable to have sex with a guy I felt so compatible with in other departments. I stopped seeing him after that night as I assumed that he would never go along with a penis reduction operation.

The Proofreader called me the next day sometime in the afternoon to invite me to his house in Muswell Hill for dinner that same evening. He was going to cook for me. As it was Friday evening, I stayed over that night, and the following night after that. Actually we spent the whole weekend eating delicious food (yes, he was an amazing cook), having lots and lots of sex, drinking wine and listening to his jazz albums. He sometimes left me alone in bed or as we were listening to music in his living room, to go and check on his Mother, who was lying motionless in the bedroom next to his. Right before he dropped me off on Sunday evening he took me up to her bedroom and introduced me to her. I was flattered and it was obviously a good sign that he had decided to introduce me after knowing me for only four days but it was kind of a weird and uncomfortable experience. She was this fragile creature, lying in bed, staring at the ceiling, surrounded by large nappies, towels and medication. The whole room smelt of a mixture of soap and antiseptics. Feeling rather confused I just said to her,

'It's a pleasure to meet you. How are you?' Unfortunately I didn't get a response.

He told me that she had been suffering from the illness for eight years now, and he had decided to take care of her when he realised that she was no longer able to take care of herself. Of course I was impressed, but honestly, I soon became aware of the fact that it wasn't all that practical and convenient having someone's Mother next door who needed round the clock care and attention when you were having sex, or were just about to sit down for a cosy, romantic meal. She wasn't like some cute little kid you could play with and communicate with on a certain level. Throughout my relationship with the Proofreader, I never really offered to help him out with his Mother or with anything else. I came to the conclusion that she was his problem, that he had made the initial choice to look after her so she wasn't in any way my responsibility.

A month into our relationship, we were spending every weekend together and also meeting up during the week as well, usually in his three-bedroom house in Muswell Hill, having endless discussions about life, relationships, our own personal experiences. I would tell him about my past relationships, sparing no details, and he would listen attentively but would later add that as a woman it was wiser not to share a historical account of one's sex life with your new boyfriend, and especially if he was Turkish. Yet he would also explain that my past was never a problem for him. He would say, 'I never seem to understand the fixation the majority of Turkish men have with virginity or sexually inexperienced women. I think the more your girlfriend has had sexual experiences, the better. It saves both parties a lot of hassle. She's more confident about her own body and knows what turns her on. At least she doesn't freak out when she sees a penis, or holds it like she's holding a hose to water the plants. But very few Turkish men would agree with me. Even if they did they'd be putting on an act. Deep down inside they would still regard a woman who's had a fair share of men between her legs as some sort of a slut. You know, some of them are even reluctant to ask their wives for a blowjob. The wife is for the missionary position and the whores at the brothels down in the narrow streets of Karaköy[13], are for all the rest. How twisted is that?'

I would sit inattentively, smoking a cigarette and sipping on my glass of white wine in his small living room surrounded by albums, books and paintings, while he would be rushing up and down the stairs, checking on his Mother, preparing the food and setting the table. Even emptying the ashtray and refilling our glasses was his task. The truth of the matter was he never asked me to help him out, probably assuming that I would come to that logical conclusion myself, but I was too immature, too inexperienced and a little bit too selfish and ignorant to do so. I was also blinded by the fact that here I was together with a man who was old enough to be my Father, yet who treated me the exact opposite of my real Father. I guess I needed to abuse the situation.

Our lovemaking sessions would sometimes last till the early

13 Karaköy is the district in Istanbul, notoriously famous for its brothels. The most renowned brothel there is the *Mektep* (the word mektep means school in Turkish and Arabic). Until not long ago the *Mektep* was where the majority of Turkish men experienced their first sexual intercourse.

hours of the morning, and I would see a glimpse of the orange sun rising steadily through the gap between the curtains of his bedroom window. And as we were both about to climax, I would beg him to come inside me. I had never wished or experienced a man to come inside me before. To tell you the truth, it wasn't all that different or noticeable, as by that time I would be considerably wet. Yet it was the idea of our bodies becoming one without any interruption or obstacle that made it all worthwhile. I was never worried about becoming pregnant, as I firmly believed that I was infertile. The actual reality of conceiving seemed so unrealistic and extraordinary to me that I could not accept or be convinced that my own body was capable of performing such a miracle.

The third month into our relationship I was giving food orders to him over the phone.

'I am absolutely craving for your Chinese noodle dish,' I would say from the phone booth near my school.

He would tell me that he needed to get the ingredients, but sure, he could prepare it for me that evening. Then I would be sitting on his sofa, waiting eagerly while puffing away on another cigarette, listening to Stan Getz or to one of his Flamenco guitar albums, as usual. By this point he would be busy in the kitchen preparing the dish. I would sometimes go over and join him there and ask impatiently,

'When is dinner going to be ready?'

Then on a similar evening, when he had laboriously prepared the traditional Turkish dish of stuffed peppers and aubergines with minced meat and he was about to serve me my plate, he said,

'I think you are pregnant.'

I gave him a surprised look before responding, 'What made you say that now? Don't be silly, I can never become pregnant.'

'Why is that?'

'I just know.'

'How do you know?'

'You know, like there are some things in life that you cannot explain but you just know?'

He glanced back at me with a confused look on his face and then responded, 'I don't know about that. But what I do know is that you're at an extremely fertile age, we've had unprotected sex on at least three different occasions and you're constantly craving for food.'

He smiled at me to ease the seriousness of the topic, as he asked when was the last time I had had my period. I obviously had no clue. The truth is I never really keep track of such small insignificant events in my life, especially the date I am due to have my period. And when I do have my periods, apart from the unavoidable discomfort they cause me, I try not to make a big deal out of the whole thing and usually forget having had them after a week's gone by. Yet it had just dawned on me that I didn't really mind being pregnant, whatever the consequences were. The mere idea that I was actually able to conceive totally astonished me. 'Could it really be possible?' I kept asking myself. So, the next day I went to my local GP. After performing a pregnancy test on me he told me that I could get the test results in a week's time. That would be just a day before the Proofreader was meant to leave for Istanbul for a month's break.

When a week later I returned to see my GP, he told me that I was just over a month pregnant.

I phoned and told the Proofreader and we met up that afternoon. I prepared myself for the worst. We had been together for merely four months so it would be natural for him to expect me to have an abortion, especially when taking into account that he was a commitment-freak. When we sat down facing each other in his living room, he smiled at me and I smiled back. It was kind of a mutual exchange of thoughts that translated into something like, 'Look what we got each other into.'

Then he started to speak and I listened attentively. He said, 'Although I've always wanted to have a family of my own, somehow it never happened. There was always something not quite right about it. Either it was the timing, or the person. It didn't surprise me one bit when I heard that you were pregnant. Who knows, maybe we subconsciously both wanted it. If you want to have the baby I'll support you in every way I can. We can get married, and to be honest with you, if it's not going to happen with you it's unlikely that I will have the chance to have a child with someone else. So it's really up to you to decide.'

After he went to Istanbul the following day, I was left on my own to get used to my new pregnant self and to decide what I was going to do about it. The Old Polish Lady believed that I had to be mad to go ahead with it; I had so much going for me. I was young, good-looking, educated and came from a good background; why on earth would I want to marry and have a child with a Proofreader who didn't make enough money and could never offer me the lifestyle I was accustomed to. Not only was he more than twice my age but on top of all this, he lived with his Mother. She said to me,

'Please, just picture yourself in a year's time in that little house of his with the baby, the Mother and him. By the way, you cannot ignore the Mother forever, you will eventually have to start taking care of her as well. If you are so mad about him, marry him but don't have his baby because then you'll be stuck with him for good.'

She probably was right in her own way but I didn't care. I was not concerned one bit about what he could or couldn't offer me. I knew I wanted to have his baby, from the moment I found out that I was pregnant.

The only doubt I had about the whole set up was whether or not I was fit to become a good Mother. Basically, I was afraid that I was going to turn out like my Father. Like him, I was short-tempered, selfish and self-centred. I didn't want to bring a child into this world knowing that he or she was going to go through the same things as I did. I was afraid that somehow my Father's foul nature was already a part of my own nature and history was just waiting to repeat itself. So I went to see a counsellor and expressed my worries to her. After listening to me for half an hour or so she reassuringly explained to me that it was normal to have some of my Father's characteristic traits, yet this didn't in any way mean that I would turn out exactly like him. The fact that I was so concerned about it showed that I was already a very different person, very different to my Father. At the end of our session she had succeeded in putting my mind at rest.

A month later the Proofreader returned from his trip. I had

already told him that I had decided to keep it in one of the conversations we had over the phone while he was in Istanbul. I had also told both of my parents that I was getting married. I mellowed things down a bit by keeping the pregnancy to myself and lowering his age to thirty-nine. Not forty-two, not even forty but thirty-nine. It was a serious marketing strategy on my part. It's an old merchandiser's trick but it still seems to work, in most cases that is. Or else why on earth would I ever have bought that hideous blouse from Harvey Nichols for ninety-nine pounds? Yet, they were not too happy or impressed about the whole thing. I think it was his profession, more than anything else that made them so wary of the whole situation. He wasn't a doctor, a diplomat or a banker. He was simply not good enough for me or my family.

After he returned from Istanbul I started to notice a gradual shift in his attitude. He would constantly express his worries, like he wasn't sure if he ever wanted a child, and I was incapable of taking care of myself. How was I ever going to be able to take care of a baby? I was going to end up running away and he would have to take care of the child for the rest of his life. It was impossible for him to look after another being besides his Mother. I tried to reassure him that that was never going to happen, but he wouldn't let it go. For a month, every time we met up, he would go on and on about his concerns to the extent that I would leave him there and then and rush back home for some peace and quiet. Once a month had gone by I realised that although I wanted to be with him and have his baby, I wasn't stupid enough to go through with it single-handedly. I wasn't scared that he would leave me on my own to take care of it; I knew that that would never happen but I needed his moral support to go along with the whole thing. I needed him to want it as much as I did; otherwise there was no point in going ahead with it and imposing it on him for purely selfish reasons. It was sad and heart-breaking, but by the end of the month, when I was three months' pregnant, I told him that I was going to have an abortion. He asked me half-heartedly if I was sure, maybe I was making a mistake? I might be a confused person who changes her mind every other minute when I have to decide over little things, like what food to order from the menu, or which pair of shoes to buy, but when it comes to life-determining decisions, when I have finally made up my mind, nothing and no one can ever make me change it again.

When we both got out of the car and were heading to a private clinic for my first appointment, he begged me to go back on my decision but it was too late. I could deal with his worries and concerns when I still had a choice, but if he was to behave the same way, later in my pregnancy when I had no choice left, I knew that he would make me miserable as hell. I was also aware that I wasn't perfect, and he had a point with being concerned about my capability, as till then he hadn't seen much of it. Nevertheless, if I was going to have a baby at the age of twenty, I needed more reassurance, trust and support than I was getting.

I was three and a half months' pregnant when I had my first abortion. It was one of the most difficult experiences in my life as I was giving up on something that I wanted with all my heart. I remember crying all the way to the operation room and when I woke up from the effect of the anaesthetic, I still found myself crying unconsciously. You see, during those weeks of pregnancy, I had lived every moment of the day with total awareness that I was carrying a small embryo that in a short time, day by day, month by month, was going to turn into a divine being. A being that I'd look at with astonishment and be able to trace certain physical characteristics, behavioural patterns to that of the Proofreader and myself. Till that day, I had never acknowledged that I had the effortless devotion of motherhood in me. I could never imagine in my wildest dreams that I was able to put all my selfish concerns aside for a single day let alone embrace living the rest of my life through another being's existence. It was so difficult to come to terms with the fact that *maybe* I had literally killed the possibility of it ever happening. In the weeks to follow my abortion, whenever I lay alone in bed and closed my eyes I would see this re-occurring image: a piece of bloody flesh that would fall out of nowhere with strong force and hit my bare stomach.

I never spoke to him about the effect the abortion had on me. He suggested that we ought to get married anyway and who knows maybe we could still have a baby in the future? I would just listen to him without saying a word. We continued to see each other as if nothing had changed; we even went for a week's holiday to Madrid together. Yet a lot had changed for me, and during the few months after my abortion the initial attraction and devotion I had for him gradually turned into hate and disgust. I would slam the door forcefully once I was in his silver Hyundai when he'd pick me up from school.

'Hey, easy! Are you trying to break it?'

'Shut up!'

'Aren't you going to give me a kiss? Or at least you can say, hi, how are you today...'

I would just give him a dirty look and respond by yelling as hard as I could, 'Shut – the – fuck – up!'

Needless to say I had lost any sense of respect towards him. Although I would still spend some weekends at his place, sex was never on the menu. I guess he was aware of the fact that I needed some time to recover so he never pushed me, yet when he mentioned one day that he missed having sex with me I told him that I would only sleep with him if he was willing to pay for it. At first, he thought I was kidding. He held my hand and as he leaned towards me to give me a kiss, I pushed him away and told him that I was bloody serious. It wasn't that I needed the extra cash or had some hidden fantasy to become a prostitute. Neither was I intending to make a living out of his small contributions. As it was never about the money, I was always reasonable in terms of how much he could afford. After all, I knew that he never earned more than two thousand pounds a month so I would charge him a hundred pounds, or fifty pounds or sometimes twenty pounds, depending on what day of the month we were in.

At first, he would ask me in an embarrassed manner how much I was going to charge him that day and I would always get the money up front. His hands would involuntarily wander into his wallet to check if he had the exact amount and as soon as he did I would grab it off him and quickly place it in my purse and then we would go upstairs to his room. I still enjoyed having sex with him but it was the satisfaction I got from fulfilling my intention that really made it worthwhile for me rather than the physicality of the whole experience. My intention was to cold-heartedly humiliate and belittle him; put him in a position where he was unable to have sex with the girl he was so in love with, without paying for it. I guess I was taking revenge, in a rather twisted way. I didn't really care what he thought or if he ever got my point. For me, he was just stupid and blind enough to play along with my games – and that was good enough for me.

4

The Bangladeshi Landlord

I met the Bangladeshi Landlord on a Saturday evening when I happened to be seated next to him in the dining section of Tramp. I had arrived there with an Iranian businessman, a guy half my height and twice my age who spoke continually about anything and everything. I usually would switch off about half an hour into our meeting as it was too draining to listen to everything he had to say. But he was okay. At least he didn't come onto me and he knew a lot of people and therefore was fun to be with. So it was his friends we had come to join in Tramp after feeling somewhat bored in each other's company at Morton's in Berkeley Square. The table was a mixture of Asian/Middle-Eastern businessmen with their professional blonde girlfriends for the night. I kind of felt out of place, as my friend suggested that I squeeze into the seat next to the Bangladeshi Landlord, being surrounded by all these ageing dark skinned men with their heavy accents, laughing and joking around with each other, wearing shiny, expensive tailor-made suits, and smoking and waving around these massive cigars that were probably much larger than their manhood. I didn't know if everyone seated at that table was a multimillionaire, but it was obvious that that was the image that they wanted to project. I knew that I did stand out from the other girls at the table; I was a brunette wearing a rather conservative black cocktail dress that showed relatively little flesh. As I exchanged a few sentences with each of the men seated at the table, I did so in a serious and cool manner, in order to set the record straight that I was not a working girl out to get a client, but merely there to have a good time and enjoy myself. As for the Pamela Anderson lookalikes that were surrounding our table, I simply chose to ignore them.

After joking around with his friends and laughing so loud that I was convinced that his laughter was heard in every corner of the room, he sat up straight, turned around and looked at me with a mischievous expression on his face. He asked me where I was from.

I said, 'From Turkey.'

'Ahh, our brother nation,' he replied.

As we began to chat I started to examine him from head to toe. He was a tall, heavily built man with a dark complexion that created an almost illuminating effect in contrast to his grey-white hair and white beard. You could say that he was quite good-looking with a straight, well-defined nose and full lips. He was wearing a three-piece suit that he had had made for him by his Italian tailor in Milan. Though what really stood out and caught my attention and continued to do so for the rest of the night, as we spoke, was the Rolex watch he had on his left wrist, that was imbedded with sparkling diamonds, not just the watch itself but the strap as well. I had never seen a man wear such an expensive piece of jewellery. Let's put it this way, it wasn't a watch that any man could normally carry, apart from Elton John, and I personally find it a bit over the top and uncultivated for a man to wear something like that. Yet with his larger-than-life presence it somehow suited him.

He asked me what I was doing in London. I told him that I was studying. Did I have a boyfriend?

'No, I don't have a boyfriend.'

'How come?'

'That's such a clichéd question to ask.'

He smiled before taking a puff from his cigar and then added, 'Why is it a clichéd question?'

'Because, it's a typical question a man asks a woman at a nightclub. So that he can persuade her that he's genuinely interested in her. That he's willing to ruin the rest of his evening by listening to her go on and on about her unfortunate love life.'

'Maybe I'm just curious.'

'I don't have a boyfriend and I don't intend to have one either.'

'My God! You're a tough cookie.'

'Coming from you, I take that as a compliment.'

'So are you a lesbian, or do you, as you say, intend to become one?'

I rolled my eyes and then replied, 'Apart from Sharon Stone, I don't think I would ever have the stomach to sleep with another woman.'

'So you don't want a boyfriend, nor do you want a girlfriend. Sweetheart, what is it that you really want?'

'I want to get married.'

I don't know why I said it, I suppose I just felt like saying it; maybe his Rolex watch had all of a sudden inspired me to do so. I asked him what his profession was but I was unable to get a straight answer. Though what I could tell from our first encounter that night was that he wasn't a man that took himself or life all too seriously. Later I would find out that he owned a large piece of land with villages and farms in the rural outskirts of Dhaka. He also had served as the Minister of Finance in the past and still attended the cabinet meetings of the ruling party in Bangladesh at the time.

The next day I received a dozen yellow roses. For some reason, unlike most women, I'm never too impressed by flowers. What is one to do with a bunch of flowers? Okay, I know that you're supposed to place them in a vase filled with water and put them somewhere so that you can take a look now and again and think of the guy. I suppose that I'm not the romantic type because I find that flowers are nothing but a nuisance really. For most of the time I completely forget that they're there even if they are right in front of my nose, and I find it such a hassle to change their water all the time. Actually the only time I ever think of the guy is whenever I have to change their water, but I can reassure you that it's never in a good way. If a guy really wants to have some sort of an impact on me he's better off to send me a box of Belgian chocolates, as long as I am not on a diet, which I never am although I usually pretend to be. Then I can promise you that his efforts will be much appreciated. I gave the bunch of yellow roses that the Bangladeshi Landlord had sent me to my new landlady who was an Argentinian in her late sixties. At least she was going to enjoy them more than me. By this time I had moved out from the flat in Islington and into a house in Chelsea. I never had the same bond with my new landlady as I had had with the Old Polish Lady, but it was all right, I needed my own space anyway.

That same evening he came to pick me up with his chauffeur-driven, navy Bentley. We had a couple of drinks and a few nibbles at the bar in the Dorchester Hotel on Park Lane and by the time we turned up at the exclusive restaurant of a famous London chef we were both already quite full. As the waiter came up to take our orders he said, 'Tell the chef that I am here and tell him also to prepare something special for us.'

He was obviously trying to impress me but I had no clue as to who this world renowned celebrity chef was. I just assumed that he was this miserable, poor guy working behind the scenes of his lavish restaurant, in a steaming hot kitchen in order to please his rich customers and make ends meet. Well, to a certain point I was right. As the waiters brought our starters and we managed to scarcely taste a tiny portion of the food, he asked me if I was hungry to which I replied, 'No, not really.'

He told me that neither was he and we both started giggling like children. After a while the waiter came up to see if everything was okay, as both of our plates were still full. He said that everything was fine but that we simply weren't all that hungry, in a rather joking, sarcastic manner, and asked the waiter to bring the main courses. Our barely touched main courses were also sent back to the kitchen as we were sipping our wines and kidding around, acting like spoilt rich little brats. The head-waiter came to say that the chef was wondering if everything was okay. It was all a bit of nonsense really but I was having a hell of a good time. I had found my ideal playmate. You see, what I loved about the Bangladeshi Landlord was, despite the fact that I was in the company of a powerful, rich man in his mid-forties, I had no concern whatsoever about behaving. I could be my natural, childish, spoilt, crazy self and actually be praised for it. As we were into our desserts, well not literally as we hadn't touched any of it, he told me that he had booked us a suite at the Dorchester Hotel. I wasn't ready to sleep with him but I knew he was harmless and I was having way too much fun and didn't want to go home just yet, so I accepted.

After having a couple more drinks in this grand yet not so tastefully decorated large suite, we retired to the bedroom. As he started to undress, I realised that he really didn't have a figure to die for. He was considerably overweight, with a huge bulging tummy and had a distinctive scar right in the middle of his chest. I asked him what it was and he told me that he had had a heart operation some time ago but it really was no big deal. I kind of felt disillusioned, as till then his three-piece tailored suits had done a hell of a good job in disguising his extra weight. I was already in bed undressed down to my underwear when he came and lay down next to me all naked. As he started to kiss me I told him that I was not ready yet. He asked, 'But, why?'

Unfortunately I had to explain to him why, until the early hours of the morning. It was too soon for me, I had to get to know him better first, I wasn't ready yet; basically the usual lines women have been coming up with for centuries. He wasn't aggressive about it or anything; he was just this eccentric, hyperactive, curious man who could dwell on anything for hours on end.

On our second date, after nibbling on a variety of rich French dishes and drinking red wine and fine cognac at the Le Gavroche Restaurant in Mayfair, we headed off to Tramp to meet an Indian friend of his who was a film producer in Bollywood. On our way there he said,

'So, are you going to spend the night with me tonight?'

'Hmm, let me think. Why do you ask me that now?'

'Just curious.'

'It's a really difficult question to answer. Like what if I said yes now and then you did something later on in the evening that really pissed me off, and I decided to change my mind?'

'Why does everything have to be so complicated with you? If you say yes now, you can always change your mind later. It's not like we're signing a treaty here.'

'Well, even if I were to sleep with you I'd never do it without a condom.'

'Why not?'

'What if you're infected with HIV?'

'Do I look like a person who has Aids?'

'No. Actually, you look more like a person with Hepatitis C. Have you ever been tested?'

'Are you taking the mickey?'

'Perhaps.'

'Have you used a condom with all your boyfriends?'

'No, but that's not the point. Plus you're not my boyfriend yet.'

'Yet? I like the sound of that. It gives me hope.'

He told the driver to take us to a sex shop in Soho and then turned round to me and said,

'Woman, I have never used a condom in my life! But I can make an exception for you.'

In the rear-view mirror of the Bentley, I could see that the driver was quite bemused by all that was going on. As the driver parked on one of the side streets somewhere in Soho, he handed him a fifty-pound note and told him to get a few packets of condoms. He said, 'I want a variety of condoms, with different shapes, colours and flavours.'

He had a very distinctive style of expressing himself. He would speak slowly putting emphasis on each and every syllable while he took a puff from his cigar and gazed out into the distance with a mischievous, naughty look on his face. Five minutes later, the driver returned with a plain white plastic bag full of condoms. As we were heading towards Tramp the Bangladeshi Landlord shuffled his hand in the plastic bag and opened one of the packets eagerly and after unwrapping a condom from its shiny plastic sealed case, started to examine it with great fascination. He was smelling it, touching it, to get a feel of its moist texture. Then he looked up to me and said, 'I don't know about sex, but these are ideal for making balloons,' and started to blow it up.

I also got a condom out and began blowing into it with all my force. Then after many efforts at trying to keep a straight face the driver finally cracked up and started laughing out loud.

I had to let go of my large see-through balloon unwillingly as the Bentley stopped right in front of the club. The doorman of Tramp appeared in an instant out of nowhere to open the back door of the Bentley in order to let us out, and we had to act like complete adults as we made our grand entrance into the club. And it was a hell of an entrance we made, faced with curious onlookers as we headed towards a table in the dining area where his Indian Film Producer friend stood up to welcome us. I have to admit, we did stand out together: a middle-aged finely dressed tall Asian man with his eye-catching red Hermès tie, three-piece tailored pin-striped navy suit, shiny diamond cuff-links, wearing a chunky diamond and sapphire encrusted watch on his left hand (which was different from the one he had on, on the night I met him), with a tall, young, twenty-one-year-old brunette on his arm, wearing a red Moschino cocktail dress and black stilettos. We were all very flashy.

When we were into our second bottle of white wine his Indian friend looked at him in a rather concerned manner, then leaned towards me to ask discreetly how much he had been drinking so far. I hadn't really counted but I assumed we had had a bottle of wine between us at dinner and a few glasses of cognac after that. He quietly whispered in my ear,

'He shouldn't be drinking so much.'

I asked him why but he looked at me for a second as if he was just about to say something and then turned to his friend and started talking about something completely different. I wondered what it could be but thought it was best to just let it go.

Two hours later, we were in bed, in the bedroom of a large suite at the Lanesborough Hotel by Hyde Park Corner. We were still very much dressed as we were both too wasted to get undressed. I was lying on his chest while he was gently stroking my hair. When I looked up and gave him a soft kiss on his lips I suddenly felt a strong electric shock that shook me from head to toe. I anxiously looked up and said,

'What was that? Did you feel it too?'

And then in a matter of seconds, it happened again and

again so I jumped out of the bed and said nervously, 'It must be the bed. There is something wrong with the bed. Don't just lie there, get up!'

Yet he seemed to be ignoring all my warnings. He just kept lying there as he held onto his chest, gripping it tightly with his right hand. I was confused and really didn't know what to make of it. The most ridiculous scenarios rushed through my mind as he lay there submissively, allowing his body to be overtaken by whatever it was. Then it stopped. He was still holding onto his chest and breathing heavily. I figured that I should keep quiet until he got himself together as by now I assumed that he knew what was going on.

He asked me to bring him a glass of water. I rushed to the mini-bar and poured a bottle of Evian water into a glass and quickly went back to his side and gave it to him. He stood up in bed and drank the whole glass in one go and placed it firmly on the side table. Then he started to explain. No, it wasn't aliens, demons, ghosts or anyone who was trying to assassinate him but a small battery device that had been placed into his heart in order to control and regulate his heartbeats. After having had three major heart attacks, his doctor had advised that this was the best solution for him. I asked him why he still carried on drinking and smoking as much as he did to which he replied,

'I'm not scared of dying. I will not restrain myself from the pleasures this world has to offer. I don't give a shit about the future, for me what's important is how I make the most of the present.'

Shortly after that we both fell asleep with the bag full of condoms by our bedside.

The next morning as we were having breakfast in the living room of our suite, he asked me if I would like to join him in Dubai for a few days. I told him that I had a heavy schedule at school and only could come for the weekend. He said, 'Well then, just come for the weekend. I'll arrange your ticket.'

I said that I'd think about it. Later that day he flew back to Bangladesh. When I told a few girlfriends that I was seriously thinking of joining him in Dubai, they thought that I had to be mad to trust a guy I had barely known for more than a week. One even suggested that he could kidnap me and I would never be able to return to London or ever see my family again. The fact that I was a woman travelling to the Middle East to meet up with a Muslim man had instantly inspired her to come up with this clichéd scenario. I was certain that I would be well looked after and that I could trust him, so when he called me the following night from his house in Dhaka I told him that I had thought it over and had decided to join him in Dubai for a weekend break.

I have to admit that, considering the seven-hour flight back and forth to Dubai, it was a bit crazy to just go there for the weekend, but that made it even more worthwhile. Yet, even though I had the advantage of flying first-class with Arab-Emirates, I spent the whole of the seven-hour flight smoking and drinking Scotch whisky, unable to calm myself down and fall asleep. While the lights were out and everybody else was fast asleep, I was so stressed out to the point of paranoia that I would shed little teardrops of fear every time the plane went into turbulence. I would promise myself that if I came out alive I was never going to board another aircraft ever again; but I am never all that good at keeping my promises which are made in the heat of the moment. I thought of how many trains, coaches and camels there would be before I made it back to London. Actually it could turn out to be quite an exciting experience. I would have to be dressed from head to toe in white linen as I took a ride on a camel through the desert and maybe I could even stop over for a day to see my parents in Istanbul on my way back and show them my desert tan. Probably not such a good idea as then I would have some serious explaining to do. By the time the plane landed, I had barely the energy to carry my small suitcase and myself, through customs. He picked me up with a friend of his. We were to stay as guests at his friend's house for the weekend.

Once we arrived at the house I took a quick shower and went straight to bed. Then as I was about to fall asleep, he entered the room quietly and lay down next to me. I told him firmly that I needed to sleep but he insisted that he had something to tell me. Couldn't he tell me a few hours later? No, it had to be now. As we were both lying on our sides facing each other, looking into each other's eyes while he was gently stroking my hair, he said,

'I've been doing some thinking. I've been married twice and have two wonderful daughters from my first marriage, and a son I adore from my second marriage, but they're all grown up now. I know, with my condition I'm not going to live very long. It's inherited. My Father also had a very weak heart and died at the age of forty-three so I'm lucky to still be alive.'

As he continued to speak his eyes were full of warmth and affection. 'I feel a very special bond with you and would rather spend the rest of my limited time with you than anybody else. You're very different from the women I have been with until now. I want us to get married and have a child, preferably a daughter. I'm sure our kid would turn out to be beautiful. And your life will be secured forever, you'll become a young rich widow when I die.'

I was touched and didn't know how to respond. I just smiled and gave him a kiss on the lips and told him I needed time to think it over.

After I had slept for five hours, I got dressed and went over to join him and his friend in the living room. They were both sitting in separate large identical beige sofas that were situated next to a large open veranda that was overlooking a private road with sky-high palm trees. He told me that we were going out for a drive; he wanted to give me a brief tour of the city. We drove around for an hour or so, but it was really pointless as I was too dazed to really become aware of my surroundings. All I can remember were these massive skyscrapers, which didn't really impress me that much. Maybe it was more the case of the lack of vibe this sterile, modern, pre-planned city had to offer than anything else that made me feel so indifferent about it. Then he parked the car in front of a shopping arcade and we went inside. As we were walking around aimlessly, he stopped for a moment to look at some watches that had been put on display at a jewellery shop window. I thought to myself, 'Doesn't he already have enough?'

In the course of less than two weeks I had already seen him with three different diamond-encrusted watches and I assumed he probably had a few more in stock. He told me that he wanted to take a look at something so we went in. He asked the shop assistant for a particular ladies Rolex watch that was on display.

As soon as I heard him say it I was ready to faint. My body started to feel all tingly and my heart was beating like crazy. After examining it for a while, which felt like forever, he turned around and asked me if I liked it. Liked it? I needed only a mere second, a single glance to fall completely in love with the blindingly sparkly object he was holding in his hand. It was almost identical to the one he was wearing that night I first met him, but a slightly smaller version. I said, 'It's okay.'

He then asked me if I would like him to get it for me to which I replied, 'I don't know. I'll have to think about it. Maybe it's a bit too much for me.'

'Are you sure?' he asked.

I nodded.

He looked quite surprised and handed the watch back to the shop assistant and as we were heading out, I felt extremely saddened that I had deprived myself of an object I desired to have so much, but I couldn't have possibly reacted any other way. It was true that besides his Bangladeshi roots, it was his glamorous lifestyle that had been the main attraction for me in the first place, but in order to receive such an expensive gift from a man, I believe you have to earn it, one way or another. And by 'earn it' I mean that you have to give yourself emotionally or physically, or preferably both, unconditionally. At the end of the day, everything in life is a give and take, and however painful it can be at such times to reject such temptations, I cannot take if I am somewhat uncertain of whether I will ever be able to deliver. He had opened his heart to me, but I was doubtful about whether I could ever do the same. I wasn't even sure whether I was ever going to see him again when I returned to London. If I had accepted his gift I would feel obliged to do so and I wanted to have the freedom to do as I pleased. It was too much of a high price to pay for some stupid watch.

Yet, having said all that, the temptation I have had from an early age, for expensive consumer goods, designer clothes and fine jewellery, has always created a personal conflict within me. You see, by nature I am an extremely greedy person. When I go into Gucci or Fendi, I'm never totally satisfied by buying a single item; I simply want to have it all. I have been a loyal purchaser of *Vogue* magazine since the age of fifteen and have performed a particular ritual, ever since. As soon as I get hold of the latest issue, I run back home and start flicking through the pages quickly, choosing every single item that I would want to have, which is usually anything that's wearable and any item which would not make me look like a complete freak. Then I imagine that by some magical force, once I go back to my bedroom, they will be all lying there on my bed waiting for me. Or when I am by myself on a bus or in a cab, passing through Sloane Street I play this game where I have the option to choose either side of the street and I persuade myself, for a few minutes, that I can have anything I want from the shops that are situated on whatever side I have initially chosen. I usually go for the left side as it's got Harvey Nichols to start off with. But what about the Graff Jewellery that's on the right side of the street? Just imagine lying in a bed full of Graff diamonds, now wouldn't that be a treat? I guess it's some kind of mental masturbation and it's silly and pointless but I just can't help it.

I am a consumer junky and believe me, I'm anything but proud to admit this to you. Why do I give so much shit about a piece of fabric or some stupid stone? Why do I find it so difficult to get the bigger picture? That in fact I am the perfect female prototype of a capitalist society. I really loathe myself for that. And even when I do get the bigger picture once in a while and think what it would be like if I left everything behind and moved to Tibet or Cuba, I know that I would never have the balls to do it and that next season you are very likely to bump into me at Harvey Nichols as I make my way to the dressing room, holding a mountain of clothes.

I guess, growing up as a diplomat's daughter, living a privileged life, chauffeur-driven cars, maids, beautiful homes in the most distinguished and sought after areas in town, embassy cocktails, had all had a substantial effect on me. Although it was never meant to last forever and it never did (my parents finally settled down in a three-bedroom apartment in Bebek), I was never able to fully accept it. After my Father's retirement, I still wanted to continue to live the lavish lifestyle I had become accustomed to and when I split from the Proofreader, I consciously chose to associate myself with rich and powerful men who had a chance of offering me just that. Yet the problem was that I wasn't ready to sell my soul for it. I wasn't just after the lifestyle but wanted the whole package, which is so hard to find; a man who could offer me both his money and his soul. The problem with rich and powerful men is that they become so infatuated with their own power, the endless possibilities that money has to offer them, that somewhere along the line they lose their sensitivity towards the more profound values in life. To such an extent that in the end they transform into soulless creatures that are unable to relate to anything deeper than their wallets. After the initial excitement of meeting someone of that calibre and spending nights and days fantasizing continuously about how our first date was going to turn out, I usually would end up feeling disillusioned on our date, becoming totally convinced that I could not possibly bear the person's presence for another hour, let alone a lifetime.

Even so, by no means was the Bangladeshi Landlord such a soulless man. Although his soul had been damaged to some extent, it still had been able to sustain a certain delicacy, sensitivity and passion towards life. Yet, whether it was his bulging tummy or some other reason I was consciously unaware of, I just wasn't physically attracted to him. Nevertheless I decided to sleep with him on my last evening in Dubai. After all, you could never be a hundred per cent sure without trying. That evening we had gone off to a Chinese restaurant at some five star hotel to have dinner with a Bangladeshi couple that were based in Dubai. Both husband and wife were in their early forties. After we had gone through the surface of things the wife turned to the Bangladeshi Landlord and said with her strong Bangladeshi accent,

'Well, it's definitely a delight to see you happy like this after such a long time.'

He nodded as he answered back, 'I have asked her to marry me this morning...'

She jumped in without giving him a chance to finish, 'Well, are you going to marry him? Did you accept his proposal?'

Had I? Well, to tell you the truth, I really hadn't come round to thinking about it. I replied, 'Well, I have to think about it.'

Then she said with a sarcastic grin on her face, 'All the girls are after this man. It's difficult not to be tempted. After all, diamonds are a girl's best friend.'

As soon as she mentioned the word 'diamonds' I realised once again the excessive amount of diamonds, emeralds and rubies she was covered with and said to her, 'I love what you're wearing. You must be really into diamonds yourself.'

She nodded quietly. Somehow my remark had wiped off the annoying grin she had on her face. Then we returned to more mundane topics, like comparing restaurants in London and Dubai; it was better off this way as no one would get offended.

After carefully monitoring his alcohol consumption throughout dinner, as I had no intention of being electrocuted once again, I gave him the signal by going into bed all naked and asking him to get a condom, which he did reluctantly from the medicine cabinet in his friend's bathroom. During our sex session where he did most of the work and I tried ever so hard to get into it, I felt like my body had lost all its senses. As he went down on me, I thought to myself that he could be licking my nose or my eyebrows and it most probably would create the same sensation. More so, I could be a news broadcaster at CNN, giving an update on the horrific events occurring in the world or doing a presentation at school, in front of my tutors and classmates without a blink of an eyelid. As I moaned now and again in order not to be too impolite, in my head I was questioning how different men and women were from one another, or were they really? Would a man still enjoy a blowjob from a woman he wasn't particularly attracted to? Well, it probably depended on how drunk he was, but generally speaking he wouldn't really mind too much or at least he would eventually let go and say to himself, 'I might as well enjoy it.' Maybe the difference stems from the fact that men, unlike women, have not been brainwashed to justify every single sexual encounter they have. They could be fucking a cheap slut, or an ugly chick or in worst cases, Daisy the Labrador. At the end of the day, they could always dismiss their actions as a heat of the moment thing.

Then I told him that it was time for him to wear the condom.

'Shit! I was trying to make you forget about the condom!'

'Just wear it, will you?'

He got up on his knees. The sound of tearing cellophane, followed by the sound of a man struggling to put on a tight, plastic shield around his dick were good enough to help me visualize what he was up to in pitch darkness.

As soon as the noise had stopped, I stretched out and held him from his armpits, pulled him towards me and allowed his penis to slide into me. I have to admit that he was quite talented when it came to using his tool so I decided to fantasize about this tall, muscular German guy I kind of fancied at school. As my thoughts oscillated between fantasy and reality I would switch on and off from feeling excited to feeling numb. Nevertheless, I eventually had to give up the German guy fantasy as it wasn't going to make me come, and after an amazing performance of fake orgasm on my part, assuming that he had done his job, he came. At that moment I knew that this was the only time we were ever to have sex. He got up and switched on the light by his bedside table and removed the condom from his penis and started to examine it. He said, while looking at it from various angles,

'Isn't it amazing that it's full of millions and millions of sperm?'

'Yes', I replied, it was all very amazing, but could he now go to the bathroom and flush it down the toilet? As a condom full of sperms is not the most pleasing thing to look at, let alone examine.

After I arrived back in London, he would call me every night from his home in Dhaka and we'd talk at least for an hour. Sometimes he would repeat himself and tell me the same story over and over again. At such instances my mind would wander elsewhere and I would think about the amazing phone bill he would need to pay at the end of the month or whether I was going to get a brain tumour from being so long on the phone. When he returned to London two weeks later, he came to pick me up with his chauffeur-driven navy Bentley from school. It reminded me of my primary school years in Vancouver when my Father's driver would drop me and pick me up every single day from school with a black, bulletproof-windowed Chevrolet station wagon. Sometimes a police car would escort us as well. All the other kids naturally assumed that my family was loaded. The boys examined the car with great fascination and envy. I tried to explain to them that, in fact, the car wasn't ours, it belonged to the Turkish government but for some reason they never believed me or understood what I was going on about. As the driver opened the door to let me in I was aware that everybody I knew and didn't know was staring at me. I felt slightly uncomfortable about it but soon got over it once I was inside. He gave me a warm hug and said that he had missed me a lot. I just smiled. Then he told me that he had attended a meeting of the ruling party in Bangladesh just before he left town and when one of the ministers had asked him why on earth he was travelling to London, he had explained himself by saying, 'I'd rather look at my Turkish girlfriend's beautiful face than you ugly buggers' faces.'

I assume that they weren't so amused by his honest yet harsh remark. He asked me where I wanted to go and I told him that I'd like to be dropped home. Maybe we could meet up later, I was tired. For a whole week he picked me up from school only to drop me off home. I was always too tired or too depressed or too something to meet up with him later on in the evening. Then after finally having dinner with him the night before he left again for Bangladesh, he asked me if I wanted to stay together with him that night. I said, 'I'm really feeling tired.'

He said with a sarcastic tone, 'Okay, I'll drop you home but we will be able to have sex when we're married, right? You know, at least we need to do it once in order to have a kid.'

I admired his ability to see the funny side of things.

After a week had gone by I felt that I was actually missing him. Why was I being so difficult? Okay, I wasn't in love with him but I did love the fact that he was in love with me. I also really enjoyed spending time together with him so maybe this was enough after all. I mean enough to marry someone. So when he invited me over to Bangladesh for a week's break, I accepted. Though to be quite frank with you, I was rather shocked when he came to pick me up from the airport in Dhaka with eight bodyguards that were heavily armed with machine guns. As a Turkish diplomat's daughter I was naturally used to bodyguards, yet the bodyguards I was accustomed to had small guns that were neatly tucked under their suits. His bodyguards looked more like field fighters. Was I in any serious danger here? Well, even if I was I couldn't do much about it so I tried to restrain myself from staring at their machine guns for too long.

When we arrived at his mansion in Dhaka, I was somewhat disappointed. It didn't look at all as I had imagined. It was dark and stuffy with thick wall-to-wall beige carpets, extravagant Italian antique furniture and dark green velvet curtains. It just seemed to be at odds with the warm climate of the place. It was also surrounded by badly done large portraits of family members. Yes, very tacky indeed. Including the bodyguards, the cleaners, the cook, the gardener, the driver, the masseuse, he had twenty-one servants at his command, living under his roof. All twenty-one men had very dark skin, piercing black eyes and anorexic-like daunting figures. After chatting to me for an hour or so he excused himself and told me that he had to check on his younger brother who was very ill, living close by. He was going to leave me for a couple of hours but when he returned we were going to drive to his place in the country.

When he did get back sometime around early evening, I was sitting aimlessly asking myself what on earth I was doing there after watching the whole trilogy of *The Godfather* on video, and ordering ice-cream but being unable to eat it as it smelled and tasted really weird. Some movies have a profound effect on me and *The Godfather* is one of them. Whenever I watched the movie I would lose myself and have a totally new perspective on life. Yes, halfway through the first sequel, while I was lying on his bed, I decided there and then that I was no longer going to be just an ordinary student but instead a tough, cold-hearted businesswoman, as soon as I got back to London. Just in a matter of a few weeks, I was going to transform myself into a ruthless mafia boss that was going to lead a complex drug operation, bringing lorries full of heroin, hash and opium from Afghanistan that would pass through Turkey and make their final destination, London. But wouldn't I kind of feel guilty about selling hard drugs like heroin and opium? Well, let's face it, it's a cruel world no matter what I do; it was about time that I toughen up a little. And no one was going to have the balls to fuck with me. I would have the toughest bunch of Turks and Kurds in East London working under my wing, who would kneel down out of respect and tremble inside with fear whenever they were in my presence. Of course I had to change my body language and the way I spoke in order create such a persona that could intimidate and boss around all those savage bullies.

Whenever I had to pause the video and go for a desperate pee, after having held it for way too long, I would practise my new self in the mirror, while feeling the ecstasy of finally releasing my ever so concentrated fluid.

'Don't fuck with me!' I would say out loud while giving myself a dirty look in the mirror.

Not quite right, do it one more time. Say it slower, with a dead cool expression and maybe you can lift one eyebrow in order to give more emphasis. Okay, do it now, one more time. Finally having finished peeing I would flush the toilet, lift up my trousers and go closer to the mirror.

'Don't fuck with me you son of a bitch or I will make you regret you ever lived!'

Yes, much better, but then again there is always room for some improvement. Promise to practise some more once the movie is over?

'I promise.'

Less than an hour after he returned, we were on the road inside a very large Range Rover with five of his servants. Another Range Rover was escorting us as we were driving through a bumpy dark narrow road. Besides me, everybody in the car was armed with machine guns including the Bangladeshi Landlord. I had asked him earlier on why he needed so much protection. He had explained to me that there were a lot of powerful people, including some ministers from the ruling party that wanted to force him to give up the large chunk of land that he owned. Three years ago they had even kidnapped his son and kept him hidden for six months. But it hadn't worked. Although with me he was like a careless spoilt kid, I realised that deep down inside he was a tough, stubborn man who valued his pride and dignity above anything else.

After an hour into our drive when I was just starting to warm up to the whole situation, our car suddenly lost its balance and started to move uncontrollably from side to side. Was it my destiny to die in a Range Rover full of men and machine guns on the outskirts of Dhaka? What would my Father make of it? Let's face it, if I were to die at that moment, it would be far more impressive than to be randomly hit by a bus when crossing the road on Oxford Street.

Then after struggling with the wheel, the driver was able to stop the car right in the middle of the road. The other car stopped behind us as well. Everybody apart from me got out of the car to see what was going on. Apparently one of the back tyres had come off. Now and again, I looked back to see what they were up to as I felt uneasy about being stuck in the middle of nowhere. It was hard to distinguish the faces of his men; their faces seemed to blend in with the darkness of night. With their white tunics, they all looked like faceless ghosts floating in mid air. I wondered what they thought of me. I assumed that they saw me as this highly capable prostitute that their boss had brought all the way from London to satisfy his sexual needs. They were strict Muslims, I was a girl having pre-marital sex; it was impossible for them to see me any other way.

Less than half an hour later we were back on the road again. On the way he explained to me that his land consisted of three villages. All the villagers who resided on his land were working for him. He had sugar plantations. He also had mango plots.

'Do they all have a fixed salary?' I curiously asked.

He told me that he didn't pay a single dime to anyone who was working for him; he just supplied them with food and shelter. I felt shocked by the injustice of the whole set up. While he travelled first class all around the world, ate at the best restaurants, and basically enjoyed the finer things in life, he had people working under him like slaves. These people had no control whatsoever over their own future, they just had to keep on doing what they were doing in order to survive. It was unfair but I wasn't there to start a revolution so I kept my thoughts to myself.

After a few minutes had passed by I asked him, 'So, where exactly is your house? Is it in the centre of one of your villages?'

He looked at me with the usual mischievous expression on his face and replied, 'You know, we Bangladeshis are very loyal to our roots and traditions. All the villagers live in mud houses, including myself. Have you ever seen a mud house or been inside one?'

'No,' I replied with the sudden feeling of panic that had awakened in me.

'I can enjoy the comforts of a privileged life when I am at my home in Dhaka, or when I'm travelling, but when I get back to my land it's a different story. For my villagers to respect me and for them to regard me as one of them I have live under the same conditions as them.'

I asked hesitantly, 'Well, is there a separate toilet in your mud house?'

'A separate toilet? My sweet girl, out in the wilderness you have the freedom to take a leak or a dump wherever.' He took a puff from his cigar, looked straight into my eyes and having noticed the look of despair and terror in them, started laughing hysterically.

I said, after taking a deep breath, 'Okay, very funny...'

'I got you there for a few seconds, didn't I?'

Once we entered his land, we passed through one of his villages where I saw a few villagers walking around; the women wearing dresses made from the brightest colours of emerald green, turquoise blue and fuchsia pink, and the men wearing long white or beige tunics. Then, as we were passing through a narrow road that was surrounded by sugar canes on either side, he told the driver to stop the car and open up the roof. He picked up his rifle firmly, got up and pointed it out to some target at a distance. He said that he had just seen a wild boar, but it was too dark to trace it and it most probably had disappeared after being alarmed by the loud engine of the car.

As we continued to drive along the narrow road and make our way to his home, which he so often called 'my headquarters', I asked him why he had tried to shoot the wild boar. Was it because of its meat or the fact that it was a dangerous animal to mankind? He explained to me that wild boars were the biggest threat to his sugar plantations. Not only would they feed their large appetites by chewing into numerous sugar canes, but once they were done with their feast, they would do somersaults and be tossing their huge, heavy rounded bodies from one side to another and continue to destroy the rest of the crop nearby. I found it amusing that these animals acted like a bunch of drunken hooligans who had no limits and who would misbehave and trash the place after having way too much to drink. Finally we arrived in front of a large set of gates where two men with machine guns were awaiting. When I looked up, I also saw two more of his men sitting up on top of two separate white towers, monitoring the whole place. One of the guards below pressed a button for the gates to open up and we slowly drove inside.

As it was pitch dark by now, it was difficult for me to make a thorough account of my surroundings. They had lit up parts of the garden, the massive pool and the entrance of his house, which was highly influenced by middle eastern architecture with its minimalist white walls, flat cement roof and arched windows and doors, yet it was difficult to make out the rest. We sat down on the large cushions by the pool and his servants started bringing out endless trays of food. It was late evening so there was a slight cool breeze in the air. He asked his men to quickly set up a fire right in front of us so that we could warm up a bit. He was just about to dig into his plate full of rice and fish balls, when he said, 'We are no longer in London. Here it is customary to eat food with our hands, and woman, you should do the same,' and then he took a handful of rice and squeezed it firmly by making a tight fist with his hand and then started to bite into it.

Okay, I respect that each country has its own customs but eating greasy food with your bare hands was something I found very difficult to relate to. Ever since I was a little girl, I remember the expression of disgust on my Father's face whenever I reached over to take a piece of chicken wing or a grilled sardine. Although I find many of my Father's actions towards me as being on the wrong side of the track as a parent, his insistence on having table manners is not one of them. I think it's rather crucial to bring a bit of elegance to the dining table as otherwise the brutal physicality of our animalistic urges for survival might make themselves way too obvious. I asked the Bangladeshi Landlord for a knife and fork and tried to hold myself back from looking at the grease that was dripping from his fingertips, but it was too late, my mind had already registered it.

The next morning when I woke up and went outside to join him in his garden I was mesmerised by the beauty of it. Rows of roses and palm trees that seemed to stretch out to infinity. And the high walls that guarded his headquarters were adorned with begonias in the brightest of all reds and eye-piercing fuchsia that was so intense in colour that it became painful to look at after just two seconds. There were also wild cats and squirrels running around and about the place. After we had our breakfast he showed me around his rose garden, sometimes stopping as we went along the narrow cement path that was surrounded by various types of roses on either side, to show me a particular one that he so much admired, whether it was for its orange, pink thick petals or its divine aroma. And while he continued to do so, he would take endless photos of me. At first I was a little self-conscious but soon got used to it, and to this day, whenever I get a bit nostalgic and go through my photo album and come across these photos, once again I become aware that he was able to capture the essence of me, the real me, in those pictures he seemed to be taking so randomly.

During the day, I would sometimes notice the strange look on his servants' faces whenever I screamed out loud as a response to something he'd just said. It was kind of awkward the way we communicated with each other, the giggling, the shouting, the way we laughed till we almost cried and the funny, indefinable noises that would come out of us.

One evening, around two in the morning, when we had a considerable amount to drink and we were just fooling around, being our usual silly selves, he said that he needed to go with his men to shoot some wild boars; it was totally fine with him if I preferred to stay behind. I had never gone hunting or experienced a gun being fired and this was the perfect opportunity. He said, 'Are you sure woman? I don't want you to freak out.'

'Remember? I'm a tough cookie. I can handle it.'

Okay, let me just tell you that I did naturally freak out a bit. We were driving very slowly in pitch darkness with four of his men, one on the wheel, two in the back holding onto their shotguns, and one dangling his bare feet next to me (luckily he didn't have smelly feet), sitting over the open roof of the car, holding a torch, while the Bangladeshi Landlord was directing him, in their own dialect, as to where to point it. They were listening attentively to the sound of the night and as soon as they heard a crack from either side of the rich sugar cane plantation or saw something move, they would ask the driver to stop the car and have a look around. Then finally at one such point the Bangladeshi Landlord got up from his seat, took his aim and fired a shot and I nearly peed in my pants. Luckily, he was too occupied with his mission to take notice of the extremely frightened person who was seated beside him. It was the instant yet deafening loud sound coming from his shotgun, and my mixed feelings about an animal being killed right there and then, that had scared the living daylights out of me. The guy holding the torch quickly jumped off the car and made his way into the sugar plantation in order to see whether the Bangladeshi Landlord had hit his target. Yes indeed he had. I asked him what was to become of the lifeless wild boar. He told me that they would inform the villagers who were non-Muslims, as the ones who were Muslim refused to eat pork, and they would take it back to their village early next morning and have a day's feast.

In the following days of my stay there at his headquarters, I thought extensively about what exactly I was doing there. I was there to get to know the man I was vaguely considering marrying. As he was naturally spending a great amount of time in Bangladesh my initial concern had been whether I would be able to stand the place or not. Let's be honest here, Bangladesh is not one of the best, sought after destinations in the world. It is politically corrupt and culturally unrefined. I hadn't been too impressed with Dhaka; the streets were full of disfigured beggars and the city lacked any sense of architectural consistency. Yet, once I had arrived at his land, I had been taken by the calm serenity the place had to offer. The truth is, I felt that I could live in his headquarters all year round, and maybe feel the need to visit London or some other metropolitan city when I occasionally missed the fast pace of things. The problem wasn't with the place but with the man and my feelings towards him, or better put, my lack of feelings towards him.

I did care for him but not in the way this proud man deserved to be cared for and loved. He was a man of passion and it would only be fair to respond to his love on equal terms. Otherwise I would just end up making him feel miserable and insecure, and I had no right to put him or myself through such a burden. It was unnecessary. I had a whole life ahead of me and if he had some limited time left in this world, it was better he did not waste it with some spoilt girl who had no clue as to what she wanted from life.

After I returned to London he was also back three days later. I remember it was early evening, around 7 pm that he called me while I was in my room waiting for his call. It was difficult but I had to be honest with him. As soon as I picked up his call I said, 'I've been doing some thinking while I was at your headquarters and after I returned from Dhaka. I cannot marry you or be with you. I am really sorry for wasting your time.'

As he spoke back to me I noticed that his voice was trembling. He said, after taking a deep breath, 'Let me see you one more time, just for tonight.'

When I tried to explain to him that it was pointless at this stage to see one another as I had made up my mind for good he said, 'I have to see you just one more time, that's all I want. I promise that I will never disturb you again. Trust me, I am a man of my word.'

I accepted unwillingly although I would have preferred not to see him again after letting him down like that. An hour later, he picked me up with his navy Bentley. This time round he was in front of the wheel. We didn't say much to each other as we headed to the bar at the Hotel Continental on Park Lane. Once we were seated at a table at the nearly empty bar, and he had ordered our whiskies, he took a large sip and started to express himself in the most honest and unguarded way ever. He said, with tears running down on either side of his cheeks, 'Woman, I love you like I have never loved any other woman before. I wanted to marry you and have a child with you.' And as he held firmly onto his chest he continued, 'I feel this uncontrollable pain in my chest.'

I thought, 'Shit, not again!' but luckily, the kind of pain he was referring to was emotional, not physical.

'You know, I would never have thought that a woman would

be able to get to me after all I have been through, and believe me, I have been through quite a considerable amount of shit in my life. Yet somehow you managed. Why, but why are you doing this to me?'

By this point, I was also crying. I could never hold my tears back when I saw someone else cry and on this particular occasion it was even more frustrating as I was the one who was causing all the sadness and the pain. For an instant I thought about whether I could go back on what I had told him on the phone, but even if I did it would only be a momentary solution, not a final one. So I chose to embrace his sorrow instead, and we sat there crying together endlessly over what could have become of us, had I given it a chance. Before he dropped me off he looked straight into my eyes and said, 'I will kill you if you mention tonight to anyone; I wouldn't want people to see me as some kind of a pussy.'

Four months later I was in Chelsea Farmers' Market on a hot sunny summer's day with some friends, waiting to be seated. Suddenly across a crowd of people I saw the Indian Film Producer and I immediately rushed up to him to say hi. He was pleased to see me and asked me how my studies were going and then said with utter seriousness, 'Of course you've heard of the terrible news.'

I said, 'What terrible news?' but I could tell by the saddened and thoughtful expression on his face exactly what he was talking about.

'Haven't you heard?' he said. 'Our beloved friend passed away at his home in Dhaka three weeks ago.'

5

The Italian Film Director

I loved my new hobby. Actually dating the least likely candidates was seriously turning into a lifestyle. That's how I would spend my time away from school: passing valuable moments with men from every walk of life that I had nothing in common with, yet nevertheless feeling this uncontrollable burning desire to take a peek into their fascinating lives. I wasn't interested in love, commitment, or sex for the most part; all I wanted was to gain admission into their world and enable myself to be temporarily distracted from my own reality. I would find myself French kissing the famously handsome Besiktas[14] footballer at a French restaurant by the Thames as he handfed me in the breaks while I urged him to tell me in lengthy detail his most hilarious sexual encounters ever. He said hesitantly,

'Do you really want to hear it?'

'Please, please, please!'

Or I'd be sharing an insightful conversation with the thirty-four-year-old rich, tall and handsome Harvard-educated Turkish Islamic fundamentalist while on a flight to Istanbul when I was seated beside him. We had started chatting after I'd swallowed a large glass of whisky all in one go when the plane suddenly went into turbulence. He turned around to me

14 Besiktas is one of the leading football teams in Turkey.

and said, 'You look a bit tense. Are you okay?'

I replied, 'Well, the fact that we are about to die doesn't really do it for me.' I stopped for a second, took a deep breath and then said, 'What did I just say now! I am really sorry; I shouldn't really talk like that. I mean, mention death. It's not really a pleasant topic to dwell on. Especially with someone you've just met.'

Then as soon as I finished my sentence, the plane started to shake even more forcefully; my heart was racing like mad and I started crossing my legs, then uncrossing them, playing with my hair, my collar and scratching my neck. I looked back at him with my eyes wide open and said,

'Oh my God! I take it back. Let's face it, we are going to die; we might as well be open and frank about it!'

He gave me a warm smile and said in a rather relaxed manner, 'I believe in what is written in one's destiny. It is all in the power of the mighty God. I can give you a prayer that is an extract from the Koran that will protect you.'

Then by totally disregarding the sneering look I gave him the instant the word 'Koran' came out of his mouth, he asked inquisitively, 'Have you ever read the Koran?'

'No, I am the least religious person you can come across,' I replied and continued, 'but give it to me anyway. Who knows? We need all the help we can get.'

He took out a piece of paper and a Mont Blanc black pen from the inside pocket of his finely tailored dark grey suit, wrote it down then handed it to me. I started to read the Arabic words that were written in Latin alphabet, which was all Greek to me as I don't know a word of Arabic, while taking short sips of whisky from my newly refreshed glass.

He said, 'It might actually work better if you don't drink while you're reading it,' and then smiled.

After I had finished reading, I turned round to him and said, 'So, you are a religious person. Well, you definitely don't look it.'

'How is a faithful Muslim supposed to look?' he asked with irony.

I did have a stereotypical image in my mind but preferred not to share it with him. After the turbulence had stopped or I had become too drunk to actually notice it any longer we started talking about Islam. He did most of the talking as I had nothing much to say about it. I was technically a Muslim but my parents' cynical and doubting attitude towards the religion had passed on to me. Neither my parents nor I had ever been inside a mosque except for funerals. Nor had any of us ever fasted. We also drank alcohol and ate pork (my Father could never resist bacon and eggs for breakfast). We were definitely a family of sinners.

When he asked me why I wasn't a faithful Muslim I replied, 'I have my own religion. My religion has two rules: not to harm others and not to harm myself. It's very straightforward really. I am usually good with the first rule but I sometimes have problems sticking to the second one.'

'But you pray to God; well at least you said "my God" when the plane went into turbulence, so you must have faith in God. And if you have faith in God you must have faith in his last and most profound Messenger, Muhammad?'

'Well,' I said, 'my belief in God depends on my circumstances. It's comforting to believe that God really exists but then he only exists in our minds.'

'God is a force. He makes himself visible through what he's created: the universe.'

'I can never be convinced for sure until I get a solid proof. And if God does really exist he shouldn't be mad at me for being hypocritical as it's not my fault. He is the one who's hiding away from everyone. And how come you're so sure that it was God that created the universe? Maybe it was Satan, or maybe the universe is this massive organism that popped out of nowhere? What I'm saying here is that it might well have been God who did all this, but we can never know for sure. And because we can never know, it's best to not question it too much or else one can seriously lose it, if you know what I mean?'

He looked up for a second and then responded, 'I come across your type so often. You have been tricked into believing that having limitless freedom to do as you please will in fact make you a happier person and will have no consequences whatsoever. Such doctrines that have been imposed upon us by Western man can only lead one to chaos and misery. When God sent the chosen one, Muhammad, the holy Koran, he sent it to him to inform humankind that there is only one ultimate truth and only one single path to human salvation.'

'Listen, even if there is truth in all that you're saying and that God sent Muhammad the Koran with the intention of giving mankind various guidelines on how to have a prosperous life, or how to find salvation, I am one hundred per cent certain that he doesn't expect us to follow it with blindfolded determination. I mean, for one thing, he is meant to have created the universe for crying out loud, you'd expect him to be a little bit more broadminded and flexible than that.'

Although he didn't look offended I could feel that he wasn't too happy with what I was going on about. Before kindly dropping me off at my parents' home with his chauffeur-driven black Mercedes Benz he asked me for my number and I gave it to him but changed the last digit. An Islamic fundamentalist can be an uplifting companion for someone who has a fear of flying but our discussion on the whole Muhammad, Koran, God business was enough to satisfy me for a lifetime.

Or I'd be on a first date with a thirty-two-year old Israeli banker who was working for JP Morgan, having a cosy dinner with him in La Famiglia Restaurant in Chelsea. While staring at my steaming hot plate of penne with aubergine, tomato and mozzarella I looked up at him and asked,

'Is it difficult to convert to Judaism?'

He hesitantly replied, 'Why do you ask? Do you wish to become Jewish?'

'No, not really. Well, maybe.'

'It's not impossible, but yes, it's difficult.'

'Hmm...so how long would it take me? I am quite an impatient person you see. Do you know any people that have converted to Judaism?'

'Well, I have a few friends who had girlfriends that were not Jewish and they had to convert in order to get married. It took them about two years. In best cases, a year.'

'What about you? Would you ever consider marrying someone who wasn't Jewish?' I then asked.

He looked at me with a serious expression on his face and then said, 'I can never get married to someone who isn't Jewish or who isn't intending to convert.'

'Does religion play such a big part in your life?'

'I wouldn't consider myself to be religious; for me it's more a question of identity. Plus my parents would have a heart attack if I were to marry a non-Jew. So why do you want to convert to Judaism?'

'Jewish people are quite well-known for being successful in business and I just thought...'

He jumped in saying, 'So you actually want to become Jewish to make money?'

'Is that a bad thing?'

I could see that he was lost for words so I continued. 'Well, I am aware that it does sound a bit superficial and dishonest and it probably would be a tough call to convince a Rabbi. Do you reckon that the Rabbi would see a glimpse of dollar signs glinting in my eyes? Maybe instead of converting I should just fake it. I could always turn up at any given synagogue and pretend that I am in fact a Jewish Turk, couldn't I? It's not like they're going to check my family tree, right?'

He didn't respond to my question but just smiled back at me instead. I sighed for a moment and then said, 'But the tragic truth of the matter is, even if I was to become a fake Jew or even a genuine one, I somehow know, deep down inside, that it would never work for me. I would be lacking in the identity department; if you know what I mean?'

More refreshing for me were some of the weekends I spent

with the chubby, dark complexioned, medium height and reasonably ugly forty-something Turkish Doctor who had a large appetite for life. Luckily he was married so whenever he had a bit too much to drink and came on to me, I would tell him that I could never have an affair with a married man as opposed to admitting that I simply wasn't attracted to him. We had so much fun together that I didn't want to put him down or lose his friendship. Some weekends we would go to London Zoo and run all over the place while holding hands like kids before taking a ride on the merry-go-round. At other times we would go to his empty surgery on a Sunday afternoon with a bottle of Famous Grouse whisky, get completely drunk and sing old Sezen Aksu songs to each other. His desk would be the stage where we would perform in separate go's. Or we would go to the movies before going to some random West End bar and get totally wacked to the point that we would share our most intimate thoughts. One day when we were sitting at a bar and had more rounds of whisky than we could handle he said,

'How much can I trust you?'

I replied, 'All the way.'

He then said, 'I want to tell you something that I have never shared with anyone, not even my wife of eighteen years.'

Then he just grinned, lit up another cigarette and after taking one more sip from his whisky, he continued.

'I told you before that when I was at university I was a devoted communist. Well, during those years most people were but I was more than just a passive supporter; I was in fact the leader of an underground communist group. Being a communist in those years was a big deal. It was the seventies. We were the baddies. At least that's how the Turkish government, the Army and the Police Force saw us. Riots broke out at universities all across the country between the left wing and the right wing supporters almost every other week and whenever the police intervened, it was always the communists that were beaten up severely. I was dating this girl at that time. A petite brunette with long black hair and large black almond eyes. She had this delicate and innocent look about her. To tell you the truth, I was madly in love with her at the time.'

Then he leaned back and gave me a look of doubt. I could feel that in his mind he was still contemplating whether to go ahead with his story or not. He then cleared his throat and continued.

'One sunny afternoon, when we were walking hand in hand in the streets of Ankara this police car stopped in front of us. Two officers came out and asked us for our IDs.'

After he took a deep breath he went on to explain how they were taken to a police station, placed in separate rooms and questioned for hours. Finally, the police officer who beat the living daylights out of him until he could not stand up straight, said, while he was still lying flat on the ground, 'If you're so determined not to speak, then I guess you leave me no choice but to fuck your girlfriend up her precious butt.'

'He then left the room and I could hear her cries from the room next door. You know she constantly called out my name for help?'

He went on to explain how he then traced the same police officer, killed him as he knelt down and cried for forgiveness, with a single shot to the forehead in a deserted parking lot, and how he, with the help of his comrades, buried his body on top of an existing grave at a cemetery in the outskirts of Ankara.

When he had finished with his story he just said, 'If you're going to ask me if I feel any remorse the answer is no. That bastard deserved to die.'

Naturally he called me early next morning to explain that he was drunk and didn't know what he was saying.

Needless to say, I was mesmerized by the mind-blowing personal experiences and diverse approach to life these men were willing to share with me. To such an extent that by the time I was introduced to the Italian Film Director I was like Alice in Wonderland: curious to find out what the next set of doors would open up on.

The funny thing about the way my affair started with this certain well-known Italian Film Director was that when an Italian girlfriend mentioned him, how he had a home in London and therefore visited London on a regular basis, I had practically never heard of the guy. Yet I was intrigued and kept reminding her to introduce me to him the next time he was in town. 'Why?' you may ask, and I surely asked myself the same question. He was a guy in his early sixties who had been a significant figure in the Italian film industry; yes, very big deal! Come on, when had I ever been so keen on Italian cinema? Yet, as I had spent a significant part of my teenage life in Rome, he represented a nostalgic idea of a heritage that I never fully felt I belonged to; that although a part of me looked down on it, another side of me wanted to experience it on some level. I certainly was not able to grow up with his movies, like most of my classmates had done; it was way too late for that now. But I felt that maybe by meeting him and by getting to know him I could fill this wide gap and feed my curiosity and hunger to belong to it in some other way. Yet, having said all that, the minute I was introduced to him I also knew that I was going to sleep with him.

I met him one evening not through my Italian girlfriend but an Italian property developer friend who also knew him. It is a small world after all and once you set your target, it really is not that difficult to achieve it. My target was a sixty-something-year-old fat Italian Film Director who was known as some kind of a mafia guy in terms of how he managed his big movie empire, and a cruel womaniser in terms of how he treated his women, including his wives. His first wife is a well-known businesswoman, who after their divorce set up the biggest advertising company in Italy. When I later asked a friend of his about their marriage he told me that she was extremely unhappy and it was a part of her life she did not want to ever remember or mention again. As for his second and current wife, who had been a famous singing diva before tying the knot with him, well I was told by many that she resembled a beautiful bird trapped in a golden cage, who wanted so desperately to get out but whenever she made the attempt, was threatened by him and his lawyers and was reminded that she would be left penniless and could never earn a living out of the entertainment industry in Italy due to the forceful and domineering influence he had over it. I doubt that this was true. Even if she could not get a decent settlement through the divorce, I'm sure she could work with some independent agents or record labels; she could always find someone to hire her. Though the reason that to this day she has not left him (although I have never met the woman myself), I believe, is because years of verbal and physical abuse with the addition of a highly privileged lifestyle have transformed this woman of great beauty and talent into a hopeless creature who has lost all her artistic ambitions and her strength and rationality to function as a healthy human being.

Returning to the day when I met the Italian Film Director, I, a twenty-two-year-old, was sitting in a lavish Chinese restaurant, The Princess Gardens in Mayfair, to be precise, with the two older men. Throughout our meal, he didn't say much; it was mainly the Italian property developer who spoke. The property developer was a guy who had met him years ago as he had unsuccessfully also directed a few movies while living in Rome, and then had moved to London to begin a new life. Here, he mainly made his living through renting out a few flats he owned in central London, for short terms to Italian tourists. He also dealt with the Italian Film Director's finances in London. He had been showing his keen interest towards me from the start by taking me out to nice restaurants, buying me groceries from the Italian deli La Picena in Walton Street and by bringing me white truffles from Castroni whenever he went to Rome; but still his actions had remained fruitless. I simply was not interested.

Throughout the dinner the Italian Film Director and I exchanged three or four sentences, not more. It certainly was not love at first sight, nor was it lust. He was overweight, had shoulder-length, curly white hair, was wearing and continued to wear throughout our so called 'affair' extremely dull and unflattering outfits that would emphasize his huge round tummy and short legs. He was anything but charming. He was one of those guys that would never talk; you had to practically force the words out of him. He was uptight and uncommunicative. Actually, I believe that he had some sort of a serious communication disorder.

Fundamentally he was so boring, insecure and shallow that he had created this distant, self-absorbed and highly intimidating persona so that nobody could ever find out the real him or come close enough to deciphering his true nature. I would find out later in our relationship that whenever he did unwind and become less serious he would simply do so by cursing the people around him, including myself, and giggling non-stop while doing so.

He barely asked me any questions. Probably through experience over the years, in order to break the ice, the Italian property developer was talking non-stop about everything and anything, which included me. He told him my family background, my Father's job, that I had spent my teenage years in Rome, what I was doing in London, what I was studying, where I was living and so on. Yet after some time as we were into our desserts, the Italian Film Director asked me what I was studying again, and I would reply to his question, ignoring the fact that he was given this information less than half an hour ago. Both of us knew that he hadn't forgotten; yet he had nothing else to say to a youthful, fresh-faced girl who was seated at his table.

After our first encounter, he contacted me a few days later by phone and invited me to dinner. By this time I had asked around to find out more about him. Yes indeed, he was a household name in the Italian film industry. Most of those badly directed movies from the eighties that were now shown on daytime television in Italy bore his signature. Some of my close girlfriends said that he could even make me a big star. Little did they know that that was not what I was really interested in. In my relationship with him and the other men in my life I was never driven by my interests, which many of my friends have seen as being naïve or even stupid. The reason I went after him and others, although I found it difficult even to admit to myself, was never to achieve some high goal but purely for the experience itself.

Our second meeting over dinner was as uncommunicative as the first one. This time round we had my Italian girlfriend, who knew him as well, who was talking about this and that, trying to create a bearable atmosphere as he sank his teeth into his lobster at a Conran restaurant in the West End. Another aspect I forgot to mention about him is his table manners, basically the fact that he did not have any. Elegance and any form of manners did not exist in his dictionary of etiquette. Once his food was placed in front of him, he would attack it with a vengeance like some kind of a primitive, or a man who had been left to starve for days. I was told that he came from an eminent family in Genoa so I often asked myself why he had ended up the way he had. Like in our first dinner, it was this time my girlfriend, aware of my interest in him and his interest in me, telling him what my Father did for a living, how long I had been in London, and yes I had lived in Rome, what a coincidence, we definitely had some things in common, although we didn't show it. After giving it a lot of thought and coming up with a plausible question to ask him, to my disappointment, he would simply reply by saying 'Yes' or 'No' or just nod.

While paying for the bill, he asked me if I would care to join him for a drink at his house in Belgravia, which I enthusiastically accepted. Yet on our way there, as his London-based driver was driving us, I was worried that as it was just the two of us going to his home, what would we talk about? As we entered the living room, which was situated on the second floor of his house, filled with bamboo furniture as if we were in some exotic holiday location, he asked his housekeeper to prepare us some drinks. I asked for some scotch whisky, very easy on the ice, hoping that the housekeeper would be very generous with the whisky. If I got a bit tipsy it would be much easier to handle the situation. Maybe at least one of us could unwind and if I could find him less intimidating it could maybe make it easier for me to talk about myself, which I am usually very good at doing. As we were sipping our drinks, he said he had a little something for me and handed me a small velvet box. I felt my heart racing and I knew I was blushing. For me, blushing is one of my worst personal traits ever. It's almost like having the words 'NERVOUS & INTIMIDATED' inscribed across my forehead.

I opened the velvet box and there it was: an amazing diamond ring bought from one of the finest jewellery stores in the world, Bulgari. I fell in love with the ring in that instant. It was the first piece of jewellery anyone had bought me, or more correctly put, that I had accepted from anyone. Of course I had received lots of pieces in gold and silver as a child from my family and friends but diamonds were a different story. And it wasn't just that, but the fact that receiving a diamond ring from this ageing Italian Film Director seemed to accentuate and feed into my own imagination of how our affair ought to be. The ring was set in white gold with seventy-two diamonds attached (yes I counted the diamonds, as soon as I went home that night). It was all so glamorous and exciting to receive such a present from him. He told me to put it on. Okay it was too small. Well, to be quite honest with you I have chubby fingers. After all nobody's perfect, but still, I forced the ring onto my finger, as I had no intention of spoiling the whole atmosphere of the evening and as I kept it on till I went home it was quite a painful experience. Once he had made me wear the ring he kissed me passionately, maybe too passionately. He had amazing big lips, and as they embraced mine, he sucked into mine with the same appetite he had done earlier on that night with his lobster. Yes, we were sitting on his bamboo couch, our lips locked together. Throughout our kissing session which lasted less than a minute, I was thinking what a claustrophobic effect his vacuum-like kiss had on me, and at the same time, how amazing the ring I was wearing on my finger was, a finger which had started to turn red as I have very sensitive skin. There was a constant ongoing oscillation between the two thoughts.

Then I distanced myself from him and after thanking him a million times for his present, I said, 'I think I'd better leave now.'

He looked at me with surprise, and said, 'But why? We're just starting to get to know each other.'

'I've had a wonderful evening but I like to take things slow.

Plus I have an early class in the morning.'

It was all too much for me in one night; the ring, the not talking, the kiss and all. He called his driver and told him to prepare the car. I was disappointed to see that he didn't send me on my own with the driver but came along to drop me home, as I so much wanted to examine the ring on my finger, and to take it off, as I am talking about serious pain here, but could not do so while he was still there beside me. But this was the only time he was ever going to drop me home when we met in London, as he was anything but a gentleman, and chose to do it that night purely in order to make sure that he had a good chance of getting into my pants the next time we met, by making a perfect impression on his own terms, that particular evening. As we were driving along from Belgravia to Chelsea I felt this amazing rush, my lips and finger were in pain, but it was also because I was entering a whole new phase in my life. I chose not to sleep with him that night, but I knew I was going to eventually...well actually the next time I met up with him.

After that evening he went back to Rome and started to call me on a weekly basis. As you can imagine, the conversations we had over the phone were not exciting or even informative; we usually asked each other the same questions over and over again each time we spoke, but as we only did it once a week it made it less obvious. I asked him how his work was going, to which he would reply by simply saying, 'It's going fine,' and he would ask me how I was, and I would tell him what I'd been up to with friends and school, going into more detail, knowing that he never really cared but was simply pleased that at least one of us had something to say. I also asked him when he was coming again to London each time we spoke and he would repeat the same date as if it were for the very first time.

He returned to London a month later and after an uninspiring meal with him in yet another lavish, expensive London restaurant in the West End he told me that he had booked a room at Claridge's in Mayfair for the two of us.

Once we entered the hotel room he calmly sat down on the seat that was right next to the bed and started to take off his shoes and socks. I went into the bathroom of the small hotel room that he had booked for us to freshen up, as every girl is supposed to do. After a couple more meetings with him in five-star hotels that usually took place in Rome when I went to visit him, I was to also find out that stinginess was among his other great personal attributes. Although he was loaded with money he would nevertheless always, but always, book the cheapest rooms. I can't remember what I was thinking when I was preparing myself for the big event while I was in the bathroom. All I can remember was that by this time I was on autopilot; not concerned at all with what I was getting myself into but more concerned with small details like, 'Does my breath smell?' or checking if anywhere else did just in case.

The moment I decided to have an affair with him, I left my ethics, my beliefs and my soul right in front of his doorstep. I left them knowing that one day I would eventually return to reclaim them.

As I came out of the bathroom he was lying all naked on the bed with his legs crossed and with a large grin on his face. I smiled back, slightly feeling the awkwardness of the situation, nevertheless pushing those thoughts out of my head, as now it was too late to really think twice. After all he wasn't a young boy I could push around and change my mind every other second, as I usually did with young boys. I undressed down to my underwear and lay next to him. He pulled me towards him and kissed me so fervently that I could feel his teeth biting into my lips. Yes, I knew I would be leaving the hotel with inflated large lips that night, but I also knew that this always really looked good on me. After trying to take off my bra in a few abrupt and useless attempts, he asked me to take off my underwear, which I did. Finally we were both naked in bed. As he struggled with himself to get up and place his chubby self on top of me I realised that in fact he was quite well proportioned down there. Yes, to my surprise, he had a reasonably large and erect penis that seemed to stand out from the rest of the package in a rather unsuitable way. As soon as I spread my legs wide open I felt his large manhood enter me. I whispered gently in his ear, 'Don't come inside me.' After thrusting his body back and forth not more than three times, he whispered back in my ear, 'Did you come?' I was confused but knew at that instant that I had to lie. I replied, 'Yes', and as soon as I did he told me that he was coming too. After entering inside me very quickly for the fourth time he stopped and just held still for a while on top of me, then rolled over and gave me a kiss on the cheek. As I was staring at the ceiling I became aware that the problem wasn't that I hadn't been anywhere close to climaxing but the horrible fact that *he* had done so willfully inside me. Yet surprisingly I remembered that I was about to have my period any day now, which meant that I was safe, or was I? I have to admit that I was extremely ignorant at that stage in my life for someone who practised casual sex. I simply didn't care. He again struggled with his large torso to sit up straight and then made his way to the bathroom. I went under the covers and lit a cigarette as one does after sex, usually great sex in movies, but more so every time you have sex, whether it's good or bad, if you are a chain smoker like me, in real life. When he came out of the bathroom he quickly started to dress himself.

I said, 'You came inside me. I hope I don't get pregnant. Well, if I do remember correctly, I'm supposed to have my period any day now so I guess I am safe but…'

To which he answered, 'Aren't you on the pill?'

'No, I wasn't seeing anyone so there was no point. Until tonight that is,' I replied.

He said, 'Well, you should have told me,' and I said with a little girl's voice, 'I did, I guess you didn't hear me.'

Once he was dressed and ready to go he gave me another kiss on the cheek and said, 'Don't worry, you know all my children have turned out really good-looking…'

For some reason he was missing the whole point and then he left and I knew I would not see him again at least for another month as he was flying to Geneva the next day to have his medical check-ups. I lay motionless there in bed for a while, blaming myself for my own stupidity. Yes, it was my fault. Especially after what I had been through with the Proofreader. It suddenly dawned on me how easy it was to make such a big mistake. It only took minutes, even seconds to position oneself in such a vulnerable and dreadful position. Then I decided to change my line of thoughts. I had just slept with an overweight, old, sleazy Italian Film Director. Not only was the sex unmemorable but I was alone in a small hotel room, lying in a bed which took most of the space in the room, and was maybe even carrying his child. Definitely not glamorous. I had to train myself from thinking of my current position along those lines. Otherwise I would become seriously depressed and it was pointless to become depressed as it was too late to change the story line so I simply stopped thinking about it and got out of bed and tried to make the most of the situation by making a few phone calls to friends and eating all the crisps and chocolate in the minibar.

After a week of waiting for my period, I bought a pregnancy test from Boots, and to my amazement found out that I was carrying our love child.

For the first time, we had our very own new topic to discuss over the phone which, I have to admit, we didn't really dwell upon thoroughly but nevertheless it was refreshing to talk about something that we both had in common after asking each other the usual questions. After replying, 'It's going fine' to my question about how things were at work I simply said to him, 'I'm pregnant' to which he answered back, 'All my children are really good-looking. If you want to have it, just have it. I'll support you.' I told him that I was not ready for a child, it would interfere with my studies and that I basically wanted an abortion. We both decided that it would be best to have the abortion when I came to Rome for a week before flying to Istanbul for the Easter break. He told me that he would arrange my ticket, and then hung up. I wondered why he had said that I could have it if I wanted to. I knew that he was terrified of being caught cheating on his wife, of letting everybody find out what an ageing scumbag he really was although everybody already knew. I guess it was some kind of a comforting tactic he was using towards me. Would he still have said, 'All my children turn out really good-looking' if I were to go ahead with the pregnancy? I doubt it, but I honestly didn't care. All I knew was I had to get rid of it and not think too much about the actual reality and the implications of my circumstances. Throughout the four weeks that I was aware of being pregnant, up until the day of the abortion, I never thought once that I was carrying another life inside of me, a being I could give life to and nurture, a being that had the chance to become a good-looking child like the rest of his father's children. No, my approach was very clinical. I saw it as a small but inevitable operation I had to go through, like having my tonsils removed.

When I arrived in Rome three weeks later a friend of his came to pick me up from the airport. He was a disillusioned actor in his seventies who had taken part in many theatre plays in his youth but now, with his loss of artistic drive and determination, and in order to pay the bills, he usually played minor roles in cheap soap operas. As soon as we entered his clean yet modest three-bedroom apartment, he went and put on his favourite Bach CD. We had discussed how we both liked classical music on our way to his place in the car. The Disillusioned Actor was the complete opposite of the Italian Film Director. He was a deep and fragile being who had been let down both in his personal and professional lives. I realised that his hands were shaking as he lit another cigarette. He told me that when his second wife left him, who was this ravishing Sicilian signorina and who, thanks to him, became and still is a famous actress/ singer in Italy, he was so emotionally shattered that he almost lost vision in one eye and had had shaky hands ever since. He said, while seated across from me holding his cigarette, 'The day she left me I escaped from Rome and went up to the mountains, stayed by myself without any human contact for a week. Everybody was worried sick about me. I lost my zeal for life. I could never have imagined in my wildest dreams that she would do something like that. Leave me for another man. Maybe I was too devoted to her. Some women don't like that. They prefer a man who is going to treat them mean, softies like me bore them after a while.'

All of a sudden he got up and went into one of the rooms in the back and brought an album to show me how beautiful she was as a young girl, when he had discovered her first before the rest of Italy had done. Then we spoke about his work. He kept repeating that he despised working next to the new generation of actors in Italy who had become overnight successes and who had no idea of the discipline necessary to become good actors. He hated them and the whole industry but needless to say, was drifting along with it just to pay the bills. One day he was going to leave everything, his job, the apartment, Rome, and move to Tuscany and lead a quite life, away from all the disgust he had to face up to on a daily basis in his current life. I liked him. He was refined, sensitive and had a great sense of humour. I told him that I would love for him to come and visit me and my parents during the Easter break in Istanbul to which he replied, 'I'd love that.' In that instant we smiled and stared at each other's faces, our smiles suddenly became frozen as we both realised that that could never happen. How could I introduce a seventy-year-old actor that I had met through an affair I was having with a married, old film director whose kid I was going to abort within the week? We both knew it just wasn't meant to be.

The doorbell rang. The Disillusioned Actor got up with a look of uneasiness on his face and said, 'Well, that must be him.'

He entered the apartment hitting his right shoulder on the doorframe, then the lamp, and then the coffee table as he came and placed his heavy body right next to me. He never knew how to carry himself. Like his temperament, his movements were always abrupt. The Disillusioned Actor had switched from the relaxed and friendly mood he had been in for the past hour and turned into some sort of clown/servant character, as he made stupid jokes to entertain his new guest and maybe lighten the heavy atmosphere that had suddenly dominated the room we were in. He began to tiptoe non-stop between the kitchen and the living room, constantly returning with a new plate of something he had prepared for the special occasion and making sure that everything was all right. He asked the Italian Film Director if he had had a nice day to which he replied, after taking a sip from his Scotch whisky and with a large grin on his face, 'You know, you are such a faggot, a fucking homo, you son of a bitch!'

The Disillusioned Actor and I smiled nervously at each other. Till that day I had never experienced a grown-up person cursing at another just to amuse himself. The only swear word I heard in our household as a kid was the word 'pimp' which my Father would occasionally use when he was annoyed with someone, like the goalkeeper of his favourite football team Galatasaray, or our gardener who took care of the garden in our summerhouse but who never once turned up on time.

The Italian Film Director's behaviour disgusted me yet intrigued me at the same time. He was so different from anybody else I had willingly come into contact with before. Then totally disregarding the insult he had just received, the Disillusioned Actor went on while still smiling nervously,

'And it was so nice to meet your young beautiful lady friend here. We have been chatting so nicely. She's not only beautiful but so educated and warmhearted. You are such a lucky man to have her. Wouldn't it be great if we could all meet up in London next time? Maybe I can join you on your next trip. I love London, the cafés and the theatres. It is such a culturally rich city.'

At this point the Italian Film Director turned round to me with the same grin on his face, obviously sharing the same positive thoughts his friend had just expressed about me and said,

'She is a fucking whore, who I like to fuck.'

Now, I have to admit, I certainly did not see that one coming. All I could do was smile back but I was embarrassed and didn't know how to really handle the situation. Should I answer back? Maybe I could tell him that he was a fat ruthless lonely bastard who liked insulting and belittling people because it made him forget how miserably insecure he really was under his own skin. Yet I just thought that that would not really go down too well with him.

A few years down the line I was to meet a businessman who

came from one of the richest families in Izmir and who at one point managed the most successful Turkish football team of a particular year. Although he came from an extremely distinguished family, studied in London, married a trophy wife, he would still have affairs with the most rude, slutty women ever to exist within the borders of the Republic of Turkey. I had once had the privilege to join him and his then air-stewardess mistress for drinks. All I can remember about the woman was that she had bright red hair, a nice big curvy bum and kept insulting him by calling him names like, 'you bastard, you fucking idiot, you motherfucker, you're such a loser' and many more, to which he listened with sparkles in his eyes and a naughty smile on his face. It obviously turned him on. Maybe it was all down to the fact that she was so different from what he had been accustomed to throughout his life. Maybe beneath his shiny suits and public persona, he simply was plain bored and saw her as some kind of an exotic fruit, a breath of fresh air that did not exist in his privileged life. Maybe he was secretly rebelling against his parents who were the incarnation of high-class and good manners or maybe regardless of his distinguished background he had acknowledged the fact that he was different from his roots. To have class is not something that can be imposed on you if your character does not blend in with it; you basically need to be born with it, and in his mid-fifties he had finally come to terms with his own lack of sophistication and wanted to embrace it with somebody similar to his own nature. That must be why, although his friends constantly insisted that he should end his affair with her, he kept seeing her on a regular basis for at least two years.

After the initial embarrassment of being called a 'fucking whore who I like to fuck,' next to a complete stranger who I had met practically not more than two hours ago, I took a large sip of whisky and lit a cigarette. Although his words had caused me to feel uncomfortable and question myself as to why I was sitting next to this jerk, they were not able to penetrate any further. Yes he had fucked me and would do so again that particular evening, however that did not make me feel like a whore or someone who was being taken for a ride, someone who was being used for sex. I was aware of his intentions yet they didn't bother me one bit. He was using me only because I had allowed him to do so.

After our sex session that took place in one of the bedrooms of the Disillusioned Actor's flat, while he was watching the evening news back in the living room and chain smoking, the Italian Film Director asked me, as he was getting dressed, when I would like to have the abortion; maybe it would be better if I had it the day before I left for Istanbul? I assumed he thought it would be more convenient for him. I told him that I wanted to have it as soon as possible. Then his driver dropped me to my hotel.

He called me the next day and asked me if I would like to join him and a few of the people he worked with at one of the best fish restaurants in town, Quinzi & Gabrieli, for dinner that evening. I, of course, accepted. The Disillusioned Actor was going to pick me up from my hotel to give the impression that he was accompanying me rather than the Italian Film Director. Although he picked me up on time there was such heavy traffic on our way to the restaurant that the Italian Film

Director called us twice impatiently on my mobile to see whether we were coming or not. When we did arrive, I saw him sitting at a long narrow table with a large group of people who all had very recognizable faces. They were mostly actors, TV hosts and one or two directors. He had two empty seats next to him. I sat right beside him and the Disillusioned Actor sat next to me. I have to admit that I was a bit nervous. It wasn't like I was a fan of any of them, but the fact that I was surrounded left, right and centre by some of the most famous faces on TV and the Italian film industry made me feel privileged yet intimidated at the same time. After all, for them I was just another young pretty face. Throughout dinner I chatted with the Disillusioned Actor as if it was just the two of us having dinner by ourselves. At one point the very famous comedien who was sitting opposite me with his extremely good-looking model girlfriend asked me how long I had been living in London. I answered back nervously saying, 'For over three years.'

The next morning around 10 o'clock I received a very strange phone call. The man on the other end of the line, whose voice I could not recognize, kept repeating the same question in English, 'Who am I?'

'Well, I don't know. You tell me. Who are you?' I answered back.

To which he would reply, 'Who am I?'

I am not the most pleasant of people at the start of the day and I was not really interested in being harassed over the phone by some freak even before I had had my morning coffee. I told him that I had no time for his silly games and as I was just about to hang up he apologized and said that he was the comedien who was sitting across from me at the table the night before. The Italian Film Director had borrowed his phone to call me up when we were running late in traffic and he had saved my number on his mobile. He said,

'I want to see you. When can we meet?'

'I'm sorry but I can't meet with you.'

He was shocked and kept asking me why. I told him that I was very busy and had to go so I hung up. Thirty seconds later my phone rang again. I picked up, it was him again. I guess he wasn't used to being rejected and I could understand why. He was Mr Popular, had a weekly show broadcast from Rome that everybody would tune into on Friday nights at 9 o'clock. He was a reasonably good-looking, thirty-something, hyperactive comedien who would throw himself across the stage, dancing, making impersonations, which he was very good at, and basically joke around like a mad man for an hour. He said to me, 'Why don't you want to go out with me? Are you seeing someone?'

I said, 'Yes,' although I really didn't consider myself as being in a serious relationship with the Italian Film Director, but I didn't want to get myself into more trouble. I had more important issues to deal with, like having an abortion a day later. He then said,

'Well, can I at least call you again sometime?'

I said, 'Yes,' as he was highly amusing over the phone and it was kind of cool to receive phone calls from such a famous guy anyway.

When I returned to London he started calling me at least once a week. Each time he would call he would impersonate someone, like an African American rapper or a Russian (he didn't know a word in Russian but that didn't stop him) and once I realised that it was actually him, and sometimes that took quite a while, we would both start giggling. Yet after a while his phone calls became less and less humorous and more and more about the psychological despair he was in. He never really told me what his real problem was; maybe even he couldn't figure it out. He was one of the most successful men in show business, people adored him, yet there he was calling up a girl who he had only exchanged a sentence with at some random dinner, for emotional support. Then one day he told me that despite his busy schedule, he was coming to London, just to see me. He was going to book a hotel and would I ever consider staying with him? I said, 'No,' and never heard from him again.

Going back to the not-so-pleasant day of the abortion in Rome: the Italian Film Director had told me a day before that the Disillusioned Actor was to accompany me to the hospital. I remember it was a miserable rainy Friday morning. As we were sitting in the hallway, waiting for the doctor to arrive, the Disillusioned Actor kept asking me if I was all right. I told him that I was fine. He told me how shocked the Doctor was going to be when he saw a young girl with an old ugly man that resembled an ancient fossil by her side, probably assuming that he was the Father. I smiled. After we went through the usual formalities with the Doctor and it was time for me to go to the operation room, the Disillusioned Actor gave me a warm hug and said,

'Sweetheart, I'm not going anywhere. I'll be right here waiting for you. Everything is going to be okay.'

He really was a gentle and sweet man but I just wished that he'd stop being so nice to me at that stage as it almost made me cry, and I didn't want to cry. I didn't want to show any sign of weakness. It wasn't that I was embarrassed about crying in front of him or the Doctor. I just didn't want to come to terms with the fact that I had really screwed up big time yet again and I was not strong enough to deal with it.

After the abortion we went back to his flat and I fell asleep for a few hours. When I woke up the Italian Film Director was there in the living room with a bouquet of a dozen yellow roses.

When I flew to Istanbul I decided that I didn't want to see him again. Having said that, I did meet up with him on a number of occasions then gradually broke it off by saying I was seeing someone else. I had played the role of the mobster's mistress quite devotedly and was now ready to move on. He told me that he was happy for me and that I could call him anytime if I ever needed anything.

Yet after a few months, on a hot sticky summer's day in London when I was feeling bored, insecure and frustrated and did not know what to do with myself, I called him. He was very happy to hear my voice and asked me how I was. I told him that I was fine, as I hadn't called him for emotional guidance.

'When can I see you?' he asked.

I said that I was going to Istanbul to see my parents in a week's time.

'Well,' he said, 'why don't you spend a few weeks with them and then I will take time from my heavy schedule. I can meet you in Istanbul and from there we can go to Paris together for a week.'

I accepted simply because I was bored with myself and felt like doing something radical and stupid, like going to Paris with the least romantic of all beings.

I had a relaxing few weeks at my parents' place. I ate whatever I wanted, slept for long hours, played with the dog and walked around in my pyjamas all day long. My Father was also in a considerably good mood. We hardly ever spoke and he was in his study room for most of the time without a care in the world but at least there was no family drama. Yet, my initial state of relaxation was eventually replaced by extreme uneasiness as I was getting closer and closer to the date of my departure for Paris. I was actually having serious second thoughts. He called me the night before to say that he was arriving in Istanbul from New York in the morning and we were meant to catch a flight to Paris at 10.30 am. When I hung up I realised that I would rather die than go to Paris with him. 'Why should I anyway?' I thought to myself. The few weeks spent with my family had released me from my initial sense of loss and despair that had made me call him up in the first place.

I believe that every action we take, every decision we make in life has to have a point, regardless of the fact that it might seem absurd, meaningless or even self-destructive to an outsider. A one-night stand can seem senseless to a girl who is waiting for her prince charming, yet it can be highly rewarding for someone who spends days on end masturbating in bed and who is not ready to drop her emotional guard and start a new relationship but who wants to be caressed and fondled, and physically brought to climax by a complete stranger.

I spent the whole night awake, constantly coming up with new scenarios. What if my Father had had a stroke in the middle of the night, or I had became seriously ill, or maybe, maybe what? This was a really difficult task. As we were worlds apart from one another I had to come up with a plausible story that made sense to him, not me. It made perfect sense to me that I just didn't feel like spending any time with him but there was no way I could be honest with him. I was scared of him, and I knew that I was not being just paranoid. He had been nice to me in his own terms so far, but if I didn't turn up the next day and did not give a convincing reason as to why, I knew that I would get myself into serious trouble.

After waving goodbye to my parents I stepped into the cab and told the driver to take me to the airport. The driver asked,

'Where are you flying to?'

I replied, 'To Paris.'

'Is it for work or for pleasure?'

'Neither,' I responded, and then suddenly felt this amazing urge to confide in a total stranger. I explained to him that I was going away on holiday with an old boyfriend and I really didn't want to go and I was just about to call him up and make an excuse.

The driver was intrigued. 'So in that case, should I not drive you to the airport?'

'No, go ahead, drive in that direction. I'm going to call him now. God, this is going to be a tough call! I have to be really persuasive.'

'Do you know what you're going to say to him? Have you gone through it in your head?'

'No, I'm too nervous to think. I'm going to improvise.'

As I started to dial his number, my hands were sweaty and shaking; I felt my whole body going numb. As soon as I heard his voice I turned on the waterworks. I was in a complete state of hysterics. I told him that something horrible had happened, that my whole life was ruined. That morning as I was preparing to leave the house my Father had seen my plane ticket. How come I was going to London when it actually said Paris on the plane ticket? Why was I lying to him? I was going away with a man wasn't I? Instead of looking for the ideal husband, I was acting like a complete whore, playing games behind his back. If I were to step one foot out of the door, I would never be allowed back in our house again. I told him that I was sorry, but I could never turn my back on my family. As I was crying like a mad woman, he told me that I needed to calm down and from the tone of his voice I could tell that he was concerned and saddened by the unfortunate events that he imagined had taken place earlier that morning at our household.

I said, 'I think I can hear my Father's footsteps. I have to go now.'

As soon as I got off the phone with him I started laughing like crazy and asked the driver what he thought of my performance. He told me that he was highly impressed and couldn't believe that it was all part of an act. This is the perfect example of what measures one can go to, in order to save one's own ass. Finally we had arrived at the airport and I told him to drive me straight back as I lay flat in the back seat of the car. It would be a pity for all that performance to go to waste. I called a close friend and told her that I had to lie low at her place for a few days.

My parents thought I was in London and the Italian Film Director was convinced that I was locked up at home. When he called me the next day to see how I was coping with the situation and to tell me that he had arranged my return flight to London, I explained to him that although my Father's reaction had been uncompromising and harsh, it was all because he wanted the best for his daughter. I said, 'Of all people, you must understand him as you are a caring, devoted Father yourself.'

Yes indeed, I had very strong feelings for him, but I simply could not jeopardize the relationship I had with my Father ever again. I could not conduct my life as before, however painful it was for me, we had to stop seeing each other and I had to go on a hunt for Mr Right. He said that I was a lovely girl with a good heart that deserved the best and should never hesitate to call him if I ever needed anything. That was the end of that.

6

The Night People I

I was in the first year of my master's degree in Television Studies, but had learned much more than I could bear to handle through my past three relationships than I ever had as a student. My student persona was just an undercover alias that gave me the right amount of freedom to experience what I was more intrigued by: the amazing series of personal experiences that life has to offer. You merely had to let yourself go and jump into whatever wagon that was coming round the corner. Yet so far I had intentionally jumped into three very steep, rugged wagons that had bruised me in their own very different ways. I needed time out. It wasn't that I was bailing out from it all, I just felt that I didn't have enough emotional energy left in me to deal with such complex characters and situations, and to put myself into such vulnerable circumstances, at least for a while. More importantly, it was a single phone call that really turned my life upside down. It was a surprisingly sunny, crisp winter morning in London when my Mother called to say that she was divorcing my Father. She sounded timid yet decisive as she explained, 'I was taught from an early age to endure and tolerate situations in the best possible ways and I think I did pretty well until now. I put up with my Father, then my husband. That's the role society gives to us women. There was no major incident between your Father and I that made me come to this decision. Actually, it was almost a bit of a surprise to me. I just woke up one day and realized that I had enough of it; that's all.'

By this stage, I was hanging out with the night people. People who spend their daytime sleeping or doing this and that, maybe making a little bit of money on the side by turning up at the monthly board meetings of their Father's company or doing some random job that they can boast about once they've done a couple of lines of coke. You see, with such people I didn't really have to make an effort, I just needed to show up and join the party. Yet, I tried to be a little bit selective as I was easily distracted in the company of someone who was incapable of offering me anything apart from a line of coke or a joint. I was spending most of my afternoons at a Turkish girlfriend's flat in South Kensington. She was in London to learn English but missed out on most of her classes that she had to attend on a daily basis as she usually overslept. She was a twenty-three-year-old, petite girl with black wavy hair, piercing black eyes, very pale skin, small yet firm breasts and a perky ass. Naturally I had seen her wasted and naked on more than one occasion. She wasn't beautiful and even looked old for her age but she embodied the perfect ingredients for a late one-night stand. Firm breasts and a perky ass were more than most guys could ever wish for in the early hours of the morning when the effect of drugs and heavy drinking had just started to wear off, and the few people left in the room or club were after just a bit more stimulation before collapsing into bed.

And there she was, usually standing in a corner with some friends, puffing away on her slim Vogue cigarettes, just waiting for her nightcap. She would usually speak of all the lovers and one-night stands she had had in the most frank way, without sparing any detail. Sex and drugs were part of her daily routine, so I guess it was only natural. And her manner was anything but refined. Every sentence would start or end with 'fuck', and when addressing you she would call you a 'whore' or a 'bastard' but it wasn't meant to be offensive, it was just her way of showing affection. You see, if she didn't consider you a good friend she wouldn't swear at you like that, out of the blue, in the first place. If you didn't know her well enough or know where she was coming from, you could easily be convinced that she was a call girl. Yet she wasn't; sex and drugs worked on equal terms as a numbing device for her, a form of escapism. From what? I was never able to find out.

Whenever I went to her flat, usually around early afternoon after school, we would spend hours rolling up and smoking spliffs or sometimes wait for her dealer to show up, who was always a few hours or a day late to deliver his goods. Drug dealers are probably the most unreliable salesmen in the world. They behave as if they are giving out their products for free or doing you a great favour by showing up at all let alone being on time.

After spending at least two hours or so on our make-up and on deciding what to wear, we would be ready to hit the town just before midnight. We'd head off with our high heels and skimpy outfits to some random guy's party or to join our so-called friends at Tramp or China White. I remember on one particular evening, we went to join a Turkish woman in her late twenties that we both sort of mutually knew, at China White (the hottest nightclub in town at the time), who was a well-known socialite in Turkey. Although she was based in London, her photos would appear in Turkish tabloid magazines regularly whenever she went back to Turkey. I couldn't help but wonder why she was a household name as she came from an ordinary middle-class family. A friend of hers would later explain that it was her pushy Mother who eagerly befriended the Turkish paparazzi and initiated her appearance in such magazines. She was somehow convinced that it would help her daughter find a rich husband. The Turkish Socialite had moved to London at an early age after marrying a Spanish guy who was based here and although she divorced him five years later, she chose to stay in London and set up her life here. She was living in a large apartment in Knightsbridge. Nobody knew what she survived on. When I had met her for the very first time she had told me that she was an antique dealer and made her living out of selling antique furniture and 19th century orientalist paintings to rich Turkish clients. But knowing that she never got out of bed before midday, it was somehow difficult to be totally convinced. Yet unlike the Turkish Girlfriend, she never talked about the men in her life and always knew how to carry herself. She actually appeared quite sophisticated and well-mannered. Although you could occasionally come across photos of her published in tabloid magazines in Turkey wearing nothing but a g-string bikini while holidaying in Bodrum, she still never came across as being cheap or vulgar. She was a petite peroxide blonde, had a dark tan all year round and a body to die for. She was considerably in tune with the cultural events in London, at least for a Turkish socialite, as she would randomly attend concerts and art exhibitions. I didn't know where her money was coming from but I could surely tell you what she was spending it on, as she would turn up to every occasion with very stylish designer outfits that would accentuate her petite yet well-proportioned figure.

She had invited us that night to join her and her millionaire businessman friend, who was a handsome, tall, blond, athletic-looking type of a German guy in his early forties who was dressed from head to toe in black. As we joined their table she asked me to sit beside him and told him that we were very good friends of hers. Were we? It really didn't matter, I guess she was just making small talk. After exchanging barely a few sentences with him I realised that it would be a complete waste of time to spend the rest of the night sitting next to someone with such a dull and uninspiring presence, so I looked at my Turkish Girlfriend who was sitting across the table and rolled my eyes. She responded immediately by making an abrupt movement to one side with her head that translated into something like, 'he's so boring' and 'let's go and check out the rest of the club then'. So we excused ourselves from the table, saying we needed to go to the ladies to freshen up. We returned an hour later after we had wandered aimlessly around the various sections of the club and had a few drinks. We found the Turkish Socialite and the German Businessman having a thorough and deep discussion; I couldn't help but wonder what they could possibly be talking about. Maybe I had misjudged him, maybe he wasn't all about money, good looks and the surface of things. The Turkish Socialite discreetly told me that the German Businessman had fancied me despite the fact that I had spent less than five minutes sitting next to him and he had asked whether we would be at all interested in joining him at his house in Holland Park for drinks. I said that it was fine as long as it was just for drinks.

She said, 'Don't worry; he's a wonderful guy and a gentleman. Plus, you're always safe with me.'

An hour later all three of us were in his tastelessly decorated mansion, which had a heavy influence of Bavarian style; I guess the guy was somewhat loyal to his roots. We were sipping our drinks and had been there for no longer than quarter of an hour, when the German Businessman said with all seriousness, 'For me, time is very valuable. I never like to waste it.'

Pointing at the Turkish Socialite he continued, 'My dear Turkish friend here knows exactly what I am talking about.'

I looked at her and in return she just gave me a shy smile. Feeling rather confused I asked him, 'Well, what is it that you are actually talking about?'

'Well,' he said, glancing at me and the Turkish Girlfriend, 'you both are two very good-looking girls and I'm a rich and generous businessman, so I am sure we can come to some sort of mutual agreement.'

I was shocked and disgusted by where this was going. Come on, I had sat next to him for no more than a few minutes, how on earth did he have the audacity to come up with something like that, to a girl he barely knew? There was this awkward moment of silence. He turned round to the Turkish Socialite and said, 'Please explain to them what I am trying to say here.'

Then she started to explain to us in Turkish while he waited impatiently for our decision.

She said, 'Well, he wants to have a threesome with you girls.'

I instantly replied, 'You must be joking!'

She continued, 'Come on it's no big deal, and he'll pay you much more than you could ever imagine.'

I tried to explain to her in a light-hearted manner at two o'clock in the morning that it was impossible for me to get up to something like that. Apart from the fact that I wasn't really that keen on selling my body to this German schwein and had never had any lesbian tendencies in my life, I couldn't possibly keep a straight face and have a threesome with him and my girlfriend.

She just responded by saying, 'You just need to shut your eyes and get on with it.'

Okay, now I finally knew how she was making her living and was able to afford those designer outfits; but was it worth it? I guess she thought so. I looked at my Turkish Girlfriend's face and she appeared equally shocked and as disgusted as me. I told her that it was best that we should leave before things got out of hand.

As we both got up, I said to him in a polite yet cool manner, 'Thank you for the drinks but we are not interested in your offer, so if you can call us a cab now that would be great.'

There was no point in being rude to him as by then I had realised that it wasn't really his fault. He had naturally come to the logical conclusion that as we were such good friends with a high-class hooker we were probably in the same league as her. As we waited for our cab to arrive at the entrance of his house the Turkish Socialite kissed us goodbye and went upstairs to join him in his bedroom. I guess it hadn't been a complete waste of his time after all. Just as she was leaving she made us promise that we would not repeat this to anyone. And I did keep my promise to her, not because I cared a single bit about her reputation but because I didn't want to relive the same feeling of disgust and humiliation by going over the details of what happened that night with a third party. That was the last time I ever saw her.

A few weeks later we were back at my Turkish Girlfriend's flat as usual, smoking spliff and getting completely stoned. It was a Saturday, around four or five o'clock in the afternoon. My hands had become numb from holding onto half a litre of Häagen Dazs Pralines and Cream ice cream, for God knows how long, spooning it with all my strength. Then the doorbell rang. Yes, we were expecting company, but naturally we had completely forgotten all about it by then. As soon as we heard the doorbell ring we panicked and stared at each other as if asking, who on earth could it possibly be? Should we answer it? Maybe not. Then she suggested that it might be her dealer, but no, he had already turned up last night. Stuck in our seats and trying to figure out who on earth it could possibly be that was standing out in front of the apartment, the person buzzed the doorbell once again, more forcefully, helping us to recollect our thoughts and remember that we had a guest coming over from Istanbul, a friend of a friend but nevertheless a guest; we had to get ourselves together.

She was a twenty-two-year old Turkish delight who had been crowned Miss Turkey a few years ago. She wasn't ecstatically beautiful but had an unbearably sensual look about her. Probably it was the combination of a perfect slim figure with considerably large, silicone breasts, cropped short natural blonde hair, a rosy complexion, wide innocent Bambi dark-brown eyes and sultry full lips. She had an amazing sex appeal and childish, boyish looks as well; definitely a great combination I would have thought. My friend and I honestly tried to have a straight, normal conversation with her, yet we were too stoned and eventually gave it away by giggling uncontrollably. She asked us if we had more of what we had been smoking. It was a relief to find out that she was one of our kind. From that day on we naturally started hanging out together. Then after spending endless nights together, getting stoned and pissed on numerous occasions we were back at my Turkish Girlfriend's flat again on another Saturday afternoon, talking for the very first time about our families, our friends and our personal experiences.

Then she suddenly opened up to us. She had come to London in order to get away from the rich, twisted and filthy people that she had been lately surrounded by after having been crowned Miss Turkey. She was from a working-class family in Konya, a city situated in the heart of Anatolia. Yet practically a few months after becoming Miss Turkey, her pictures were all over tabloid magazines, usually leaving a hot nightspot in Istanbul in the early hours of the morning with some popular playboy. At first she didn't mind, she even liked it; but soon it got out of hand. Of course her free-spirited ways didn't help either. Yes, she admitted, she liked to party, occasionally take drugs and if she was in the right frame of mind she wouldn't say no to an orgy either. And, well okay, she was also into women. What was wrong with that anyway, it was her body and she could do as she pleased with it as long as she wasn't harming anyone, right? Yes, we agreed. Yet, her free-spirited ways were a bit over the top for a society that's heavily imbued with back-stabbing and double standards, especially if you are a single woman.

Turkey is a country of extremes. I'm talking about a society where the vast majority still regard female virginity as being sacred. A society that is so twisted that some of the prudish girls you see walking around in the streets of Istanbul with their heads facing down, are in fact practising anal sex with their secret boyfriends in order to stay virgins until they're married. And in the unlikely case that they get carried away and ever lose their virginity, they go to a notorious surgeon's stuffy surgery, in the back streets of some dodgy neighbourhood in Istanbul to have it re-stitched before their wedding day. I am also talking of a society where in some villages in Anatolia incest is still a recurrent practice, some of the most violent and horrific incidents take place in the name of pride and honour. A girl of thirteen is raped by her Father and then becomes pregnant. But rather than punishing the Father for being such a sick goddamn bastard, the family members get together, including the Mother, aunt, uncle and brothers and sisters, and all agree that as the girl is pregnant, no longer an innocent virgin and therefore a disgrace to her family, she has to be got rid of. The task is usually given to the underage younger brother who then only serves a few years in prison for murdering his own sister. It's not an ideal plan, but nevertheless everyone can rest in peace – the pride and honour of the family is saved.

Then in total contrast to all this there is the marginal, educated, liberal middle class in large cities that try ever so hard to erase the nation's oppressive approach to sexuality from their conscience by screwing each other without a care in the world.

I am also talking of a society where the so-called upper class, the rich and the privileged minority lead the most degenerate and unethical lifestyles that would shock and disgust the most liberated and free-spirited Westerner. It's not the fact that drug consumption and sexual experimentation is an ongoing theme; it's more the case that as sex, especially female sexuality and homosexuality, is still regarded as being a taboo, it's always done in a highly intricate manner behind closed doors. It's a close-knit society of back-stabbers, who throw compliments randomly to one another at any social gathering, yet at the same time use every devious trick in the book of Satan to trip each other up.

These people spend so much time and energy trying to hide whose husband or wife they are fucking or trying to reveal, find out or simply make up who's fucking who to disguise what they themselves are up to, or to simply destroy someone else's reputation, it's really astonishing that they can make time for anything else in their lives. Especially if you are an ordinary girl coming from a working-class background and people start talking about you, slowly digging your grave behind your back and you haven't got a powerful rich family to secure your own ass once you become the joke of the town, you are basically fucked. A year after she was crowned Miss Turkey, she was also crowned a whore. The definition of a whore is a woman who has sex in exchange for money, and selling your body must be the most degrading and difficult profession on this planet unless you are cut out for it by nature. Yet, a woman who likes to express her sexuality is also considered a whore although she's purely doing it for the exchange of pleasures. She's not called a playgirl but simply a WHORE.

I never seem to understand why society considers sexually liberated women as such a big threat. Even in London, as a woman, you need to play down your sexuality, otherwise people see you as some sort of a nuisance. Although I have never been close to being as sexually liberated as Miss Turkey, I usually find it totally unnecessary to make myself come across as a woman who doesn't give herself away that easily to men. Sometimes I do, sometimes I don't; it really depends on my frame of mind at that given time, but honestly, why does it matter so much? My girlfriends usually advise me to be wise as they suggest that at the end of the day, every man wants to marry a woman who hasn't slept around. Even if you like to have casual sex occasionally you have to pretend that in fact you don't. But why would one have to hide something like that, especially from a man you are considering spending a lifetime with, your soul mate? No, you see he has to trust you. If I have to lie or pretend to be something that I am not in order to gain his trust, aren't I starting off somewhat on the wrong foot here? Well, yes and no. You see, you have to play the game according to the rules.

You know what? I don't give a shit about some fucking game! There is no public survey showing that if you marry a virgin or a woman who's had a very little amount of sexual experience that she will be more loyal to you than a woman who's had many lovers. But if you are with a partner who starts lying to you, deceiving you from day one, then I suggest my friend, you better watch your own back. The fact of the matter is, if you are so concerned with the notions of trust and honesty, then you have got to have the balls to face up to its implications and be willing to accept that your partner did actually have a life before she met you.

Yet, I also have to admit that I find it somewhat pointless to be so fixated with the whole concept of loyalty because the truth of the matter is, you can never be a hundred per cent sure that your partner is faithful to you. She might be the personification of loyalty in your eyes but who knows? She just might be preparing herself, right after you've kissed her goodbye and left for work that morning, for her fuck-buddy to come by and screw her brains out. That when you do call her to ask her if she's all right with going over to your parents that evening for dinner, so that you can watch your favourite football team's game with your old man, she is in fact taking a short break from riding another man, in your bed, as she's still on top of him, holding the phone with her sweaty little hands, telling you that it would be a good idea.

I guess, as women we are luckier from this point of view as we are conditioned from an early age to accept that it's all right for a man to play around a little, regardless of whether he is single or not. So if we ever find out that our beloved husband, the caring Father of our children has in fact been fucking around with prostitutes in cheap motel rooms, we are somewhat better equipped at handling the situation. At the end of the day the boy needs to have a little fun and maybe satisfy some hidden desire to be spanked or peed on, which he would not dare share with his wife. And even if he does, after a while it doesn't turn him on as much as it used to. Let's face it, there is only a certain length of time you can fuck the same person with the same hungry appetite. Maybe the flame will go out in a year's time or maybe it will last for ten years, but the bottom line is, it will never last with the same force as it did on day one. That doesn't mean that you'll stop loving the person or you need to start screwing around. It really all depends on the driving forces in your life and your priorities.

As a woman, I find it insane that there is still a majority of people out there that actually want to believe that by nature men are made to spread their seeds and therefore have a much higher sexual drive than women. It is not a question of difference between the two sexes, but a question of the individual. As there are men who can't seem to part with their willies, there are also women who have formed this amazing bond with their vibrators. And let's face it: whether you're a man or a woman, the driving force behind adultery is not a big sexual appetite you simply cannot feed with your long-term partner, but also various complexes and insecurities that stem from your own childhood. We human beings are way too intricate and complex to be analysed from a single viewpoint regardless of the fact that it's always more reassuring if we do.

So there was our poor little victim, Miss Turkey. Wherever she went, whatever occasion she turned up at, people would stare at her and whisper to one another once she had passed them by. As if what she had been up to wasn't enough, they would even go further and create stories of their own. One day she was in the company of a well-known couple that she had met a few days before. They had invited her out for dinner to some hot spot in Istanbul. The couple were a household name purely because the guy's family was loaded; so he was a 'somebody'. And as for the girlfriend, she came from an ordinary middle-class family, but it didn't really matter. She was dating a 'somebody' so she naturally was a 'somebody' too. It all started rather innocently, they were talking about this and that, sharing a few laughs after dinner followed by a few glasses of wine. All she remembers is going to the bathroom and then losing consciousness and falling over just as she was about to sit down at their table. Then when she did open her eyes again, she was no longer at the restaurant but in a basement room of some house that she could not recognize, lying completely naked in bed under a duvet. She lifted her head up and felt this instant sharp pain. The light hanging from the wall seemed unbearable to look at. Then she heard voices and turned her head to look around and saw the couple she had been dining with walk into the room.

The girl said, 'She's awake.' They both came up and kneeled down next to her and asked her how she was feeling. She said, 'My head hurts.' The girl explained, as she was stroking her hair, that earlier on at the restaurant she had fainted so they had brought her to their house to take care of her. Miss Turkey asked with a confused expression on her face, 'Why am I all naked, what's going on?' They said they wanted to make her feel comfortable. As she was explaining the incident to us her eyes were full of tears. She said, 'I had no idea what had just happened to me. I have never fainted in my life before and I was feeling totally fine with myself that day until I returned from the bathroom. I asked what the time was and it was four in the morning; I had been unconscious for four hours. All I wanted was to quickly leave the place and go home.'

So after asking for her clothes back and quickly taking a cab back home she spent hours sitting on the floor in the corner of her pitch-dark bedroom; it was just impossible for her to face any form of light. She just sat there shivering and crying with a blanket wrapped around her, completely unaware of what had happened to her during those four hours, but suspecting the worst. Her best male gay friend came over to check up on her later that morning and said that they must have drugged her drink with some sort of a date rape drug. The symptoms she had, a total blackout, an unbearable headache, extreme sensitivity to light and low body temperature all seemed to point in that direction. She would later find out that she wasn't their only victim. A pretty-faced TV presenter had also unwillingly fallen into their trap. Like Miss Turkey, she had no recollection of what they had done to her. But one can only assume that they both had been raped by the couple who were so bored with their lives that the only thing that turned them on was drugging and raping defenceless pretty girls.

Why hadn't she called the police? These sick people belonged behind bars not on the glossy front cover of some tabloid magazine. She sighed for a moment and then said, 'Who do you think had a better chance of winning if I took them to court? A Miss Turkey from a working-class family who was labelled a whore, a lesbian and a drug addict; or a guy who came from one of the most powerful families in Turkey and his beloved long-term girlfriend?'

Funnily enough I saw the famous couple a few months later at the bar of the Sanderson Hotel in the West End. They were sitting at the bar in a relaxed manner, sipping on their cocktails. Then the headwaiter came to inform them that their table was ready so they made their way to the dining section. It was obvious that it didn't matter to them that they had caused so much pain and disturbance in people's lives. I wanted to go up to them and say something, at least make them aware that there were people out there who knew of the perverted sick games they had been playing, but I simply couldn't. The truth of the matter is, while I watched them make their way to their table I realised that they did what they did simply because they knew they could get away with it. I guess it's just human nature. I still don't think that harming another human being would be my thing but I know that if I could get away with it there is a high probability that I would steal, cheat and lie without a blink of an eyelid.

One of the most interesting women I have ever met in my life has to be the Opportunist. She was a short redhead Turkish girl in her early twenties with these amazing, huge breasts that would stand out from the rest of her chubby, small-framed figure. She would wear large unflattering wire-framed glasses over her Tatar-lidded eyes that were always smudged all over with some bright blue eyeshadow of her choice. She usually wouldn't be too bothered about dying her hair on a monthly basis or even washing it on a weekly basis so most of the time she would be roaming around the city with greasy hair and dark roots. We were in the late nineties yet she hadn't got over the whole eighties phase and would be going to places like San Lorenzo's, Morton's, Tramp and Annabel's with dresses that had huge shoulder pads and shiny embroidery, and would also wear bright pink lipstick that would make her thin lips stand out and shine in the dark like fluorescent lights. She would sometimes not bother to put on a decent pair of shoes and would turn up at Annabel's with some cheap, plastic-healed, fake leather mules that resembled the kind that your ageing grandmother would wear when she had a few close friends coming over for tea and a bit of gossip. Yet she knew everybody in the London nightlife scene: club owners, bartenders, waiters and bouncers. She wasn't a member anywhere but if you were a friend of hers and you wanted to take your mistress out to one of the most exclusive, private membership clubs in town for the night, you could call her up and she'd arrange it for you. But you would also have to bear in mind that one day you would have to return the favour.

She was the complete opposite of me. Everybody in her eyes, including myself, was a potential candidate just waiting to be exploited in some way or another. She would sometimes randomly call me up and ask me to join her and a friend for lunch and then would come over to pick me up with some seventy-year-old Middle Eastern guy. After the guy had paid for our lunch at Montpeliano's restaurant in Knightsbridge, she would offer to drive us back in her old silver Mercedes Benz, and just before dropping him off at his apartment, she would stop at a petrol station to fill up. She would then go to pay for it but would return shortly after with a worried look on her face. For some strange reason there was something wrong with her credit card; it just wasn't going through. Naturally the guy would offer to pay, which she would accept immediately. She would repeat the same scenario over and over again with different guys, and each time I would be cringing in the back seat of the car, dying with embarrassment. So even a simple relaxed lunch with her was a pre-planned task which involved inviting the guy to take her out for lunch to refill her stomach with food and her car with petrol. Asking me to join her was a way of making the poor old guy feel somewhat privileged and entertained by lunching out with two young women.

Actually, to be quite honest with you, she was nothing but a cold-hearted greedy bitch who had no sense of ethics whatsoever, and was just out there to get her hands on anyone that had anything to offer, whether it was a diamond bracelet or a packet of crisps. She had no shame at all. She was always ready to degrade herself just to get a slice of the cake, regardless of how small the slice was. I never saw her spend a single penny on anything. If she felt like having a chewing gum she would ask a waiter or a cab driver or simply anyone that was around; but no way would she go and actually buy a packet herself. That was strictly out of the question. If she wanted a few new outfits, she would go to the crippled Indian factory owner's outlet in the East End and she could pick out anything she wished for and get it for free, but there was a catch: she had to try the outfits in front of him. Surprisingly, she really wasn't that impressed by expensive gifts; she preferred cash instead. If she were to receive a Cartier watch from some guy that was stupid enough to get her one, she would return it the following day and get a refund. Although she spent night after night in restaurants, bars and clubs, she would never do drugs or smoke or drink; I guess she wanted to be alert at all times for any opportunity that might pop up. She never lived to enjoy the present; the present was all about making the right choices, the right intricate moves in order to secure her future. Maybe it was because she had spent her childhood in the poor suburbs of Ankara. Yet, she hadn't done so badly for a short chubby girl, a girl that had no sense of style, sophistication or sexual appeal.

She had three flats in central London and had just bought another one in Paris around the time I met her. Definitely not bad for a girl who came from an uncultivated working-class background, with no higher education or a steady job. Her parents were actually quite religious. They both prayed five times a day while their daughter in London could spread her legs wide open five times a day, if given the chance, for any guy that was willing to make a contribution. You might wonder why I chose to associate myself with someone like her or why others did who were of a certain calibre: investment bankers, lawyers, diplomats and aristocrats. It was basically because she was quite unique in her own way and therefore highly entertaining to be around. For me, it was always so fascinating to see what measures she would go to in order to avoid paying for a cab fare, the intricate games she would play just so that she could make a couple of quid on the side. Regardless of whose company she was in, she would never hide the fact that she was a cheap peasant, a prostitute, an opportunist. Yet she would do it with such sarcasm that people would either see her as some crazy eccentric, or they would be uncertain as to whether she was just kidding or being serious. Either way, she had a certain charisma that came from her dry sense of humour and her strong personality; she didn't give a monkey's ass about what people thought of her as long as they were of any use to her.

When I first came in contact with her she had said to me as we were driving on Park Lane and she was behind the wheel, 'I find it really pointless having sex without getting something in return. All men are bastards and users so it only makes sense for us women to use them too. They deserve it. Wouldn't you agree?' I had made it clear to her that I was not interested in prostituting myself but nevertheless she realised that I was still a useful bait that she could use to draw men to herself. She would always ask me to join her at some hot spot in town whether it was Tramp or Annabel's or just some upmarket restaurant in the West End. You see, although she already knew that I was not interested in sleeping with any of the guys she introduced me to, the guys were never totally aware of this fact, which made it worthwhile for her to invite me in the first place. It was a good business strategy on her part.

A few months into our friendship she met a Texan millionaire. A fat guy with white hair and a white beard in his mid-fifties that had an uncanny resemblance to Kenny Rogers. She told me that she was in love while she giggled like a little girl. She was in love all right, but more with his bank account than anything else. Like most rich Americans from the south, the Texan Millionaire looked anything but refined. He would join us at Annabel's with worn-out shoes and deformed suits that looked as if they had been purchased from some department store in the outer suburbs of Dallas before being run over several times by a truck. Yet it didn't matter, she was in love and let's face it, it wasn't like she was the epitome of style so it was a match made in heaven. He would go into great detail about the amazing ranch he owned just outside Dallas and the various businesses he was involved with. He definitely was a big fish so she decided to play herself down. He didn't have to re-fill her tank when she offered to pick him up from his hotel apartment in Lancaster Gate. She would even invite a few of her rich, generous middle-eastern businessman friends to Annabel's to prevent him from taking care of all the bill. She didn't want to come across as a gold-digger. The moment she had been waiting for had arrived; after all these years she had finally hit the jackpot.

She was soon to realise that he was equally taken by her. Only a few weeks had passed when he started making plans for the future. He so much wanted her to come and visit his ranch and stay with him for at least a few weeks. They usually would be holding hands and kissing continuously in my company. I was almost becoming convinced that maybe it was the real thing after all. That somehow her initial greed to get her hands on his amazing wealth had borne fruit in feelings of love and compassion.

As he was in London to do business, he would frequently meet up with his clients to negotiate various deals. Then one day as we were waiting for him, on a sunny afternoon at the Blue Bird Café on the King's Road in Chelsea, he turned up looking rather stressed and frustrated. He had just made a deal with a client who was waiting to receive an amount of fifty thousand pounds by 6 pm that day. Yet there had been some sort of a problem with the transaction. He had been on the phone for at least two hours with his bank in Dallas and his client in London; the client had threatened to withdraw from the proposition if he didn't receive at least half of the amount by the deadline. It wasn't the end of the world but it would be simply a nuisance for all that hard work on his part to go to waste. The Opportunist held his hand and said, 'I can lend you twenty-five thousand pounds if it means that much to you?' I couldn't believe what I was hearing. He thanked her but said that he could never accept a loan from a woman. How would that make him feel as a man? It wasn't worth it. It was better off that he simply forgot about the whole deal. Then he sat there silently sipping his espresso and looking even more stressed and depressed. After a few minutes had gone by and he still had not said a word, she got up from the table and asked him to leave me some cash in order to pay the bill and said, 'Come on, don't be silly, we are going to my bank and I will give you the money. And don't feel bad about it, you can pay me back in a week's time,' and so they left.

Three days later I received a phone call from her. The Texan Millionaire was nowhere to be found. He had checked out from his hotel apartment and his mobile phone was switched off. After two weeks had gone by, we realised that he must have fled the country. Although I tried to come across as a compassionate friend who felt for what she had been put through, deep down inside I could not help but find the whole incident highly amusing. The Texan Millionaire, who was actually nothing but a small-time crook, was in fact the exact male version of her: a coldhearted opportunist that took people for a ride. It was as if I was watching a real life version of *Dirty Rotten Scoundrels* where

Steve Martin and Michael Caine famously play two con men that prey on naïve rich women in a small seaside town in the French Riviera. You just need to look close enough to become aware that London is a city that's infested left right and centre with assorted variations of dirty rotten scoundrels. Sometimes you're better off turning a blind eye.

The Turkish Girlfriend, the Turkish Socialite, Miss Turkey and the Opportunist. Whether it helped to pay the bills in this amazingly expensive city or worked as a form of carefree entertainment, a form of escapism to pass the time, sex played a major role in these women's lives. From the outside it almost seemed as if the Turkish Socialite and the Opportunist had more going for them. At least they were making easy money on the side, securing their future by commodifying their bodies. To this day, the Turkish Socialite's words still echo in my mind, 'You just need to close your eyes and get on with it'. But is it just that simple: to close one's eyes and get on with it?

I am no Pollyanna. I know that this world we live in is anything but ideal. Whether you are a hooker, a banker, a politician or a housewife, money rules. The majority of us watch the wildlife programmes on the National Geographic Channel with fascination and gratitude, totally unaware that behind the polished, grand gates of civilization, the reality of human existence is as harsh and uncompromising, and even more ruthlessly devious and complex than that of the animal kingdom. It's really difficult to have a clear and straightforward perspective on life when on a daily basis we are bombarded with 'quick fix' solutions that depend on our bank account and suggest an easy route to fulfilment. The new season's Gina stilettos, the latest edition of a Rolls Royce, a house in the Boltons, a face-lift, or even better, a rich husband or wife that can provide all that. In today's Western society, we are so blindfolded by the surface of things where money plays a key role, that like an army of robots on autopilot we live our day-to-day lives, losing along the way some of the most vital humanistic qualities that are attributed to mankind, all in the name of upgrading our standards of living. It goes without saying that life is a struggle from whatever angle you look at it. Yet for me, the real nerve-racking challenge in life lies above all in the constant struggle I am left to face within myself. To remind myself every step of the way that without nurturing my values, enriching my soul, questioning my conscience, basically referring to the key characteristics that set us apart from the animal kingdom, that like the rest, I am in the greatest danger of being unable to live the life I have been awarded, in body and soul, to its fullest.

7
The Night People II

As for the fascinating men that I came across while I was mingling with the night crowd: well, there weren't really that many. I naturally had a few unmemorable shags, and then there was the Greek Racing Driver. I think every girl needs a racing driver in her little black book just in case of an emergency. To be frank with you, I hadn't had such intense sex with anyone since the Sailor. Yet I despised him. He was a stupid rich brat who had come to London to try his luck at international stardom as a racing driver. Yes, very big deal. I never seem to understand the obsession some people have for speed. Okay, if you could sign an agreement with God where he would give you his word that you would still stay in one piece after racing around a track like some lunatic, I might actually have a go at it, but otherwise why risk it?

With the Greek Racing Driver I was definitely after a different source of stimulation. I had met him through the Turkish Girlfriend. While in a rather restless state of mind one day I had asked her randomly if she knew of any hot guys in London. She had instantly mentioned his name and was astonished by the fact that I had never heard of the guy. She had said, 'He's one of the hottest bachelors in town; all the girls are after him.'

Had she slept with him? Why, of course she had and she highly recommended him to me by saying, 'He is absolutely amazing in bed.' I wasn't too impressed when I was introduced to him at her apartment one evening. He was a thirty-two-year-old, tall, well-built guy with wavy shoulder-length black hair and dark brown eyes. He wasn't necessarily good-looking, but there was a certain look of madness in his bulging dark brown eyes, which made him not go unnoticed.

Thanks to his Father's amazing wealth he had studied in the best schools, been to almost every corner of the planet. Yet he was unrefined, arrogant and extremely childish for his age. 'What can I do?' he would brag, 'my dad is really loaded; I am just here to enjoy a carefree life.' He was a guy who simply didn't have a clue about anything. He had majored in two subjects: driving cars and screwing girls. Apart from the racing track, he would spend most of his time going out with his similarly shallow, well-dressed, considerably good-looking male Greek friends, who all smelled like they had just come out of the shower and who were in London to spend their family fortune on partying.

Yes, he was a selfish asshole, but as the Turkish Girlfriend had rightly put it, he was an asshole who was extremely good in bed. Why is it that men who are such good lays are equally great assholes? I really don't know. But what I do know is that there is an apparent connection between a man's character and his penis.

The PENIS... Sometimes I feel so lucky that I was born a woman. I'm almost certain that if I had been born a man, I would have had an erection problem. Even if I could get it up while giving myself a handjob, it would let me down in the presence of some hot chick I had brought home in the early hours of the morning after spending the whole night in Tramp, drinking excessively to boost my confidence and trying ever so hard to talk her into going to my place for some drinks later on. I would spend the whole night telling her what a hot shot I was. I would drop her hints to make her aware that she was in the company of Mr Loaded.

'What are my plans for this summer? Well, I probably will be spending some time on my family's yacht at the beginning of June in the South of Turkey. But it's too much of a family affair for me, so I'm going to rent a yacht by myself and just cruise around the South of France some time in August. I'll invite a few friends over as well. Why don't you come along and join me?'

She would smile shyly with sparkles in her eyes and say, 'I don't know, I've just met you.'

'Don't worry. You'll have your own room. I am a gentleman after all. And by the way, would you care for another drink?'

In harsh reality, the mere reason I was in Tramp that evening in the first place was that my ex-colleagues, who were feeling kind of sorry for me as I had been jobless for the past six months, had invited me there to cheer me up. So I was buying this stupid slut endless rounds of drinks, going completely over my bank account limit, with the hope that it would pay off; that at least she would see me as a good catch and let me screw her later that evening. And finally, after I had lured her into bed and was all over her, my penis would make me frustratingly aware that it wasn't up for any action. 'Come on, how can you do this to me now?' in my mind I would demand. Maybe it was because I had overdone it with my alcohol consumption that night, or it was just because I was at a phase in my life, being jobless and all, when I was feeling rather insecure and depressed. Well, I could always fuck her in the morning assuming that both she and my penis would still be up for it. But what if this was just a glimpse of what was ahead of me? What if I could never get it up in front of a woman ever again? Wouldn't that be scary?

My God! Having a penis must be such a burden. Although I have been going on about the double standards in society towards women I cannot deny the fact that men are faced with a different set of double standards too. You see, as a man you constantly have to prove your manhood. So much emphasis is given to the extension between your legs; whether it can get a hard erection, whether it can perform for a lengthy amount of time, whether it's the right size, that it's only natural that the majority of men secretly have some unresolved issues with their penises. And if a man is somewhat inadequate in that department he either denies the tragic truth and behaves like some ruthless Casanova, trying to get his hands on any woman he can and then treats them like shit for reminding him that his penis is a failure. Or being totally aware in the back of his mind that his penis is not his strongest point, he tries to cover it up by nurturing other aspects of his character. Otherwise why is it that some of the most generous, gentle-natured, sensitive and considerate men I have met in my life all have had small penises or an erection problem? Maybe I'm over generalizing but I still believe I have a point.

The Greek Racing Driver was endowed with a perfect tool, right shape, right size and hard as a rock. He could go on riding you all night long until you had to literally beg him to stop.

Having said that, regardless of the immense pleasure he gave me in bed, outside the bedroom I would treat him like he was a nobody, never show him a single ounce of respect.

He would sometimes appear out of the blue on my doorstep, and call me on my mobile phone. 'Hi, it's me. I'm outside your door. I missed you. Come down stairs, I'll take you out for a drive.'

I reply in an irritated manner, 'How dare you turn up just like that on my doorstep. I am busy. Go away!' while watching *EastEnders* in bed.

'Come on. Don't be so hard on me,' he insists.

'Well even if I do come out with you, you'll have to wait. I have to get ready first.'

'I'll wait for you baby. Take your time. You know it will be worth it,' he replies.

I answer back by just saying, 'Fine,' as if I don't give a care in the world and start running between my room and the bathroom like some mad woman once I put the phone down.

Take a shower, remove all excessive hair and while you're at it please but please don't cut your legs while shaving; the last thing you want to do is be bleeding all over your clothes. Do a bit of make up to hide your dark circles and give your face a radiant fresh look as Greek men are never into the whole grunge heroin-chic look. And don't you dare wear anything too dressy. Put on your most stylish sweatshirt, jeans and trainers just to prove to him that you haven't made an effort.

Then as I appear through the front door, I see him leaning against a wall, smoking a cigarette.

As I go up to him, he says, 'Hi baby,' and gives me a passionate kiss on my lips.

'Okay, play it cool,' I remind myself. I push him away and say, 'God, you annoy me!'

He smiles like a naughty little boy and replies, 'Why do you say that now? Aren't you glad to see me just one bit?'

I give him a dirty look and he starts giggling. He somehow likes being treated mean. I guess he is tired of girls constantly sucking up to him. Then he drives me in his silver Porsche to some bar; we have a couple of drinks and finally end up at his hotel room, which he rents on a monthly basis, at the Metropolitan on Park Lane, and spend the rest of the night having mind-blowing sex.

I would be home next morning looking as if I had been run over by a bus. What we had was pure sex and nothing more. Just hot, steaming sex.

Merely a second after entering his hotel room we look at each other and he smiles and says, 'So, what shall we do now, baby?' making it way too obvious what he has in mind. I approach him, by slowly moving my hips from side to side and whisper in his ear, 'Well, let me give it a thought,' while I grasp his visibly noticeable penis bulging through his jeans. Then I kneel right in front of him and unzip his jeans, lift my head up and say, 'Come on, feed me.' He replies while he struggles with himself to take out his well-proportioned erect penis, 'You want me to feed you baby? I'm going to feed you so good, baby. Don't you worry.' He unzips and place his warm, large piece of meat straight into my mouth and I start to suck into it. After a few minutes, feeling a slight hint of discomfort in my jaw and lips I take his penis out of my mouth, stand up straight and push him forcefully onto his bed and start to undress in front of his watchful eyes. He says while he also removes his shirt, jeans, boxer shorts and shoes, 'Baby, you're driving me crazy!' I turn the other way with a confident and ignorant look on my face. His feelings are mutual yet I dare not admit. Even in the heat of the moment, I have no intention to make him more bigheaded than he already is.

Then all of a sudden, I freeze the moment in my head, see myself vulnerably naked, standing in front of a naked young man who is lying in bed, staring at me with a lustful look. And at that moment, in a matter of a few seconds, as I did often enough, I have a thorough discussion with myself as to what I am just about to do.

All right, what the hell am I actually doing here right now? Okay, silly, of course I know what I am doing here but the question is whether it's the right thing to do. Having sex just like that? I should be ashamed of myself! Excuse me? Yes you heard me, I should be ashamed of myself! Come on, you only live once and I really enjoy having sex with him so what's the big deal? Remember what the Bangladeshi Landlord had said? Why should I restrain myself from the pleasures that life has to offer? Give me a solid reason! You're questioning yourself not because you genuinely believe that you are committing a wrongful action but because you're conditioned to believe that women are not suppose to conduct themselves in such a manner. It's not the little voice within you that's confronting you, but the big voice of social conditioning! You are a sexual person and even if you don't sleep with him tonight, which you are just dying to do anyway, you are eventually going to do it with someone else. That's just you; don't blame yourself for it, just accept it and embrace it. You know what? You are damn right.

He looks at me with a questioning face and says, 'Come on baby, aren't you going to join me?' Finally having cleared all the doubts in my head, I jump on top of him, always making sure that I am nowhere near crushing his balls, as from past experience it can somewhat ruin the heat of the moment. I start to tease his lips with my tongue, while my right hand grasps his penis and then as I sit up straight on top of him, I feel the intense rush from his manhood entering me. That first instance of penetration, considering that all the ingredients are there – mutual animalistic attraction and right amount of vaginal lubrication – is just too good to be true. Your body goes all tingly, and a certain wave that makes you feel both shivery and hot, hits you like some kind of mild lightning. It's pure pleasure.

As I am on top of him moving my body up and down I grab hold of his hands and move them all over my body. Then by the time I am about to climax I bend down, start biting his neck, then sit up straight again and hit him as hard as I can, merely half a second before I feel the amazingly ecstatic feeling of release. He says, 'Ouch, easy baby!' and touches his lips with his fingertips and has a taste of his own blood. I respond just out of politeness, 'I'm sorry, I don't know what came over me.' After going to the bathroom to check on his bleeding lips he returns with a hard on and we're at it again like rabbits.

When you have an earthshaking, purely sexual relationship with someone, you don't need to be a rocket scientist to know that it's only a question of time before the intensity of the whole thing fades away. Yet, even if all you have is just pure shallow sex, it's such an extraordinarily uplifting experience to be infatuated with someone like that. To be so overwhelmed by the experience that you stop being self-conscious about the cellulite on your thighs, or the love handles that are getting larger by the day, on your hips. No, the asshole who you look down on, makes you feel like an irresistible sex goddess who has the ability to shake the walls with her amazingly powerful libido in bed. It's not just that you are highly aroused by him, or by the mere thought of you and him, but also by your own sexual potential. You feel like the epitome of irresistibility. Cellulite and love handles? No, they're not flaws, quite the contrary, they are what makes you a real woman! You've got child-bearing hips baby! And whenever you're out and about, whether at a bar sipping cocktails with a friend, or crossing the street carrying two plastic Sainsbury's bags, you cannot help but notice the immense power of seduction you have over men. And just when you get there, at the peak of sexual narcissism, it all falls down. The heat starts to cool off. The heat lasted for only two months with the Greek Racing Driver and then I was too bothered to answer his calls and he was too bothered to turn up on my front doorstep. Soon after he went back to Athens and our paths never crossed again.

I remember this rich Turkish businessman that I had met through a friend when I was invited for dinner at Momo's in the West End one evening. He was a reasonably good-looking, forty-nine-year-old, very tall guy with short black hair and a dark complexion. He was casually dressed wearing a pink shirt, navy blazer with a pair of worn out, pale blue jeans and brown suede loafers. Throughout dinner he had chatted to me non-stop about this and that. In the early hours of the morning after we had spent the whole night drinking shots of tequila and dancing like mad in the club downstairs, he asked if he could drop me home and insisted on taking my number just as I was about to step out of the cab. He told me that he had to leave for Istanbul the next day but would be back in a week's time and would love to take me out to dinner.

A week later I was having an uninspiring dinner with him and a few Turkish friends of his that were in London for a long weekend's break, at San Lorenzo's on Beauchamp Place in Knightsbridge on a Saturday night. After dinner he suggested that we go to his suite at the Lanesborough Hotel for a one-to-one more intimate chat. Feeling in the mood to go with the flow, I accepted. As soon as we were at his suite sitting in two separate chairs and sipping our drinks, his hands drifted to his pockets and he took out a small piece of worn out white paper that had been folded into a miniature envelope. Then quietly he started to pour out the white powder inside it and took out a credit card from his wallet and neatly parted the white powder into two separate lines. Again he reached into his wallet and went for a fifty-pound note, which he rolled up with equal precision and handed it to me without saying a single word. I placed the fifty-pound note roll inside my right nostril, lifted my bum up as I leaned towards the table in front of me, sniffed a single line in one go and then handed him the fifty-pound roll back. After going through the same procedure a few more times, naturally we were chatting away like nobody's business. It was almost as if we were racing with each other to grab the words out of each other's mouth. I would listen eagerly to what he had to say but also would be waiting impatiently for him to shut up as I always had something equally or even more valuable to say to him.

After two hours had gone by without even noticing that the lower part of my nose and my lips were starting to feel numb, he said that he was going to tell me his best-kept secret but I had to promise that it would not go beyond those walls, that I would treasure his secret till the day I die. I told him that he could count on me. He then said,

'Have you ever heard of an organization called Club Moscow?'

'No,' I replied.

He continued, 'I wouldn't have thought so. It is a private organization that has a hundred members scattered all around the world. And the members are people of great power and influence, like presidents of the leading countries, scientists, media tycoons and the richest of the rich. Basically they are people who control the world. As the club only has a very limited membership of a hundred, a member has to die in order for them to consider a new candidate. From the outside, Club Moscow just looks like another elitist organization with the aim to create a platform for the powerful and rich to collaborate with one another but it's much more than that.'

I was intrigued and wanted to hear more about this Club Moscow. I asked him how he had heard of it. He said, 'I heard about Club Moscow two years ago for the first time through an old friend of my Father who was a leading Professor at Stanford. The Professor had been doing some research on the club for some time for an article he was working on, but was never able to finish it as he was mysteriously found dead in his flat one day.'

At this stage he got up and went to the mini-bar. While he was right in the middle of pouring himself some whisky, I asked, 'What was the cause of his death?'

He turned around while holding the glass of whisky in his hand, looked at me with a dead cool expression on his face and said, 'He was poisoned. They killed him because he was the only one who had the guts to reveal the true nature of the organization. Club Moscow is more than just an organization that brings together the most rich and powerful people under the same roof. Club Moscow members are all well aware that the world is too close to its inevitable end.'

'Shit, is it?' I anxiously asked.

Totally disregarding my desperate plea for an answer he continued, 'Therefore they're in the process of creating a new life on Mars that will enable mankind to survive. And the reason why they are guarding their plans in every possible way is that only the most powerful and rich of the world, the hundred members of Club Moscow and their offspring, will be the ones to make the journey to a new planet and to start a new life there.'

Oh my fucking God! I thought to myself. Did I believe him? I kind of wanted to but come on, life on Mars? It was a bit difficult to be totally convinced, even after a half a gram of cocaine. No, I was well aware that what this coke addict was going on about was probably one of the most controversial ways of chatting up and making a unique impression on a girl. Of course I could've reacted in a more cynical and doubting manner. I could've told him to stop talking rubbish and wipe the remains of white powder off the tip of his nose, but I had no intention of spoiling the flow of our conversation. Instead of questioning the whole absurdity of his remarkably insane story in my head, I allowed him to convince me for another few hours.

Yet I have to admit that I was somewhat disappointed later on, when I had mentioned his name to Miss Turkey one day. She just gazed at me with a sarcastic look in her wide Bambi brown eyes and said, 'Did he mention about Club Moscow to you as well?' He would have had to seriously watch his own back if he was revealing such life-threatening information to every pretty face after just a few lines of coke. I never saw him after that night, although I was meant to meet up with him the following evening. I was curious to find out what other stories he had lined up for me. Yet, unlike him, my body wasn't accustomed to doing endless lines of coke day after day. I missed our rendezvous the following evening because I overslept and when I did wake up eventually, a day later, and saw the number of missed calls from him I naturally called him up to apologize. Unfortunately he took the whole thing way too personally and to be honest with you, I didn't really care that much about it. It wasn't like I had closed the gates to a great friendship. At the end of the day coke had never been my thing.

Why does one do coke, I sometimes wonder? Okay, literally after a line of coke, you might be going on about how you want to change the world, help the poor in Africa and so on but the truth of the matter is, although you might be totally convinced by yourself at that point, you really don't give a shit about poverty in Africa. And if in reality you do, you just don't when you've had a few lines of coke. Let's face it; when you do coke, whatever subject you get stuck to, it's really not your sincere concern for the wellbeing of others, it's about you and what a great person you are for mentioning it in the first place. Your ego becomes the size of a football field and whatever it is that you are bragging about till the early hours of the day, the bottom line is that it's not coming from the heart; it's all small talk really and I just hate that.

Then there was the Fugitive. The Fugitive was a Turkish guy in his early thirties who had a face that literally resembled a bulldog. He was a short, pot-bellied guy whose body was covered with thick, long strands of black hair, well, apart from his light-reflecting, greasy bald head, that is. He was one of those guys you would feel ashamed to be seen with at the beach. He had arrived in London with his business partner after doing a runner by escaping through the south of Turkey with a boat, if I remember correctly, from Marmaris over to one of the Greek Islands. They had been able to flee from Turkey just before they were about to be sentenced and locked up in some ruthless prison in Istanbul for fraud. Yes, very *Midnight Express* minus the prison scenes. They were both killing time in London waiting for an exemption from the Turkish government. It wasn't as bad as it sounds, as they were free to travel to anywhere else on the planet as long as they didn't set foot inside the borders of the Republic of Turkey. Plus they had all that stolen money to spend so it wasn't such a terrible deal after all. Having said that, when I had asked the Fugitive one day if he ever regretted what he had done he had replied, 'How can I not? I wasn't myself then. I was doing at least a gram of coke every single day. It was coke that really screwed both of our lives. We couldn't think straight. We thought we were gods. I was such a violent, horrible person then. I wouldn't go anywhere without a gun and I almost shot my younger brother once just because I was so high on coke. London made me a better person. I stopped doing coke and I learned how to respect and be considerate to those around me. So I am happy in a way about how things turned out and that God gave me a second chance, although I really didn't deserve it. Yet the only thing that scares me is that if one day anything ever happens to either of my parents I could never go back and be there for them. That thought just eats me up inside.'

Nevertheless, although the Fugitive was no longer a cokehead his line of work in London was anything but legitimate. I guess once a crook, always a crook. Unfortunately, his partner in crime wasn't as successful in escaping from his drug-fuelled past; he still was a junkie who formulated his life around his drug consumption. The Junkie was a short, muscular guy covered all over in tatoos, with a distinctively large crooked nose, green eyes and long, straight black hair that he would wear up in a bun. Sometimes when I would drop by for drinks at the Fugitive's modern penthouse flat overlooking a private garden in Lennox Gardens in Knightsbridge, the Junkie would be also there, smoking and talking intensely before heading out to some nightclub to meet up with one of his prostitute girlfriends. Actually when I met him for the first time he had kind of frightened me. Just imagine this hyperactive guy standing in front of you, jumping from one topic to another in the course of less than a minute, while every part of his body was shaking uncontrollably. Definitely not a pretty sight.

He had once told me that he had never dated an ordinary girl in his life. He just could not handle it. I guess dating prostitutes gave him the freedom of being totally in control. Doing as he pleased with a woman, when he pleased. Bearing in mind that he was rarely able to get it up and actually screw them, having abused his body way too far, it was the idea rather than the physicality of the experience that did it for him.

The Fugitive would usually go for the young, clueless, student types who had just arrived in London from Croatia or Russia and who were struggling to pay for their tuition fees with the little money their parents were sending them on a monthly basis. The Fugitive was the man who could put all their worries to rest. Finally, instead of living in some rundown hostel in Earls Court while trying to juggle their studies with their shifts in some tacky pizza place owned by some Middle Eastern sleazy guy, they could enjoy a bit of what London had to offer. Unfortunately they soon would be made aware that nothing in life is for free. Yes, it was all great moving into the Fugitive's penthouse apartment literally a week after they had met him; being able to say 'fuck you' like Julia Roberts and walking out on the sleazy and equally bossy Middle Eastern restaurant owner, roaming around the city in the Fugitive's latest edition Ferrari and hanging out in the best restaurants and private nightclubs. Yet, too soon these girls would find out that there is no easy ride in life. Regardless of the fact that the Fugitive would provide these girls with financial security, they would run off usually after a couple of weeks or, in rare cases, after a few months had gone by. They just couldn't handle the abuse. I remember how the Fugitive had confided in me one day over lunch that he had beaten the living daylights out of his seventeen-year-old Russian language student girlfriend who was this pale skinned, fragile creature, how he had cut her long, blonde mane with a pair of kitchen scissors when she had arrived home one night towards four o'clock in the morning, after going out with his friends. He had said, without a trace of guilt on his face, 'I don't know what got into me. I just lost it. After that I called one of my friends and asked him to take her to the hospital. I knew that she wasn't fucking around or anything because she was with my closest friends, but I just couldn't handle the fact that she hadn't had the decency to call me to let me know that she was going to be late. Stupid bitch! She made me lose myself.' He definitely had an interesting approach to the whole incident. He regretted what he had been pushed into doing.

Both the Fugitive and the Junkie were not exemplary citizens and they could easily be ruthless mean bastards towards any woman if you ever gave them the chance, but if you made them fully aware that you were a woman of principle they would never try to cross the line with you. I think that's a very crucial point if you are to mix with their kind. They would not harm you if they respected you and you had to be constantly aware of that fact even if you were stoned out of your brains in their company. So as a woman how do you gain the respect of such guys? Well, to put it frankly, you basically don't sleep with them. Even if you are the woman of their dreams, the future Mother of their unborn children, from the moment you let these men between your legs, in their minds you are instantly re-evaluated and placed into an inferior category of the human race. You are no longer an individual but an object of a certain functional use to them. And even when you don't have sex with them, you also need to persuade them that you are a tough cookie who is in total control of herself and who values her principles above anything else. You basically become one of them and don't show any signs of weakness until you gain their true friendship and trust. And you'll have to bid farewell to all your feminist views and some of your ethical values right on the doorstep, before setting foot in their world. Otherwise don't even bother going in. It's not like you can change them so what is the point? It's funny how once you understand how their mind functions, how they perceive life, you realise that these people are not that profoundly different from you, that you can actually form a friendship on a certain level with them.

The urge to dominate and abuse is embedded in each and every one of us, and at times one can be tempted to cross the boundaries of civilized human behaviour. To abuse another being, whether physically or mentally, can easily work as a brain-numbing device. It can distance you from yourself and put you in a temporary state of ecstasy. It's almost an out-of-body experience. Yet after you've passed your initial state of ecstasy, you then have to face the inevitable downfall, as soon as you become aware that you have behaved like some ruthless barbarian towards a defenceless being. You become utterly disgusted with yourself. By tormenting another being you don't just harm them, you harm yourself as well. It's all very destructive from whatever angle you look at it. Yet soon after, you find your own redemption by totally blocking the whole incident from your own conscience, or by simply persuading yourself that you had been a victim of provocation.

I found it rather stimulating to hang out with such men, and to experience, to a certain degree, the world through their rigid lenses. I didn't find their wrongful ways towards women offensive on a personal level. Naturally I was aware that I was being a total hypocrite.

The Fugitive would say to me often enough, 'Up until now I've never had a female friend in my life. It's really strange that when I'm with you I almost forget that you are a woman. Did you have a sex change or something?'

'Am I suppose to take this as a compliment?'

'No seriously, when I'm with you, I feel as if I am with one of the boys.'

Many evenings we would hang out in the lap-dancing club, Stringfellows, in the West End while they would eagerly try to get the mobile number of any stripper that gave them a slight hard on and I, after too many glasses of whisky, would merely see the topless women that I was surrounded by as a part of the decoration.

After months of hanging out with the night people, going to the same venues, always coming across the same miserable faces and getting totally wasted till the early hours of the morning, I finally got bored with the whole scene. So I broke off all my ties with the night crowd. I even changed my mobile number. They probably saw me as a traitor but I was just tired of abusing my body and wasting precious time. In fact I was so off the whole London nightlife scene that I firmly believed that I could not set my foot in another night club ever again; which was just a phase, but God knows I needed it.

Round the time when I started to focus on my studies and spend evenings at home studying, reading books or just watching TV, I met a young business analyst while pushing a trolley at my local Sainsbury's. He was a twenty-nine-year-old Turkish guy who was living at a house owned by his family on Sydney Street in Chelsea. He wasn't good-looking or anything; actually he looked like a bit of a nerd. He was slightly shorter than me, was balding prematurely, wore glasses; he was basically your average guy. But at that stage in my life I needed a well-grounded person, a mummy's boy, a guy who had family values, a guy who wasn't into partying and who would spend the whole week working like a slave and spend his weekends roller-blading in Hyde Park, going to the movies or having dinner with his equally average friends.

Usually we would meet up during the week to watch a DVD while lying down on his couch, and end up going to bed around 10.30 pm. Weekends were equally uneventful but sometimes we would share a bottle of wine at his place after having dinner with his friends in Itsu or La Famiglia. Over the weekends I would wake up before him to prepare him a richly assorted breakfast of freshly squeezed orange juice, bacon and eggs, croissant and jam, and would even cook dinners at his place for him and his friends. Yes, in just over a month I had transformed myself into a Stepford wife. On Sundays when his friends came over to his place to watch Galatasaray versus Fenerbahce, I would sit quietly, only interrupting them to see if they wished to have something to drink. On weekdays when he lay motionless in bed after a hard day's work at the office, I would give him a thorough massage so that he could have a good night's sleep. I was too good to be true. Tidy, caring, easy-going, loyal and attentive; what more can one guy want? I remember when we had gone for a weekend's break to Paris and we were having a cosy dinner in Buddha Bar, he had said to me, 'If we keep on seeing each other for another two months I think that we could start living together, and if that goes well we can then get married.'

At that moment I knew that I had to give him the bad news as soon as we got back from our romantic weekend break, before things got out of proportion.

Yes, in a matter of nine months I had gone from one extreme to another, which has always been my signature style. Had I learnt anything from my experience? Well, as a matter of fact, I had. Funnily enough the greatest pleasures in life are achieved in the simplest ways as long as you are open to them. A walk in the park, feeding the ducks at a nearby pond, a cosy, simple dinner among friends, a good novel, watching your favourite TV series while drinking hot chocolate in bed, all have the potential for brightening up your day. Maybe my relationship with the Business Analyst never had the potential to flourish into a lifelong commitment, but it made me become aware that the route to happiness is through creating a healthy balance in your life by having the ability to appreciate the more mundane things in life. Though I have to admit that this is easier said than done, or maybe it just hasn't really worked for me because I have split-personality disorder or something. Well, I have had my moments but up until now, my life has been anything but ordinary. Yes, one part of me wants just that but the other part, which seems to have an overall domineering influence on me, is not so easily seduced by the mundane things in life. Why else do I have the impulse to do the unthinkable, the unacceptable; why do I have this strong desire to go to the extreme?

I think one of the greatest virtues in life is to know oneself. If it's happiness and fulfilment that we're talking about, then it can only be achieved by knowing who you are and what really does it for you because, like most things in life, it's all very relative. And if you have no clue as to what does it best for you, you can spend the rest of your life trying on various personas and situations to see what fits best, like you do when you don't know what you want to buy, but end up staying for two hours at Harvey Nichols only to buy the most hideous outfits ever. And in both cases all you will ever end up with will be this unbearable feeling of emptiness and a loss of direction.

8

The Prince

I met the Prince through a Lebanese guy I used to know who owned a stunning flat in Cadogan Square. He wasn't just any other Lebanese guy, but a man in his mid-sixties, who only mingled with the right crowd; that being royalty and the elite. He spoke eleven languages fluently. He definitely was a character. Apart from having extremely refined manners he also had a trained voice that everybody would be made aware of at one point in the evening as he would sing old ballads like *Moon River* or *Strangers in the Night* with his trained, very high-pitched voice. He also had an impressive repertoire of jokes that he could go on and on telling until somebody had to literally ask him to stop. Though that rarely ever happened. He was a naturally gifted entertainer, yet for some reason he had ended up in the wrong profession by becoming a surgeon. He was usually off to some exotic destination, always catching the cheapest flights available from Gatwick, to be a guest of honour at some elite event. He was a dignified version of the amusers, one of a few I had had the privilege of meeting. You can come across these men, and they are usually men, at the most sought after spots around the world. They will be sipping a cocktail by the pool at a five-star hotel in Miami, or on some private yacht belonging to a millionaire tycoon anchored off Mykonos, or skiing with a personal instructor in St. Moritz. Yet they won't have to pay a single dime for anything, everything is already taken care of. All that they are expected to do is turn up and entertain their rich and famous friends.

Some of these men have made a serious living from the entertainment business. They are not just amusing but, through years of hardship, have acquired the skill of reading people as if they were an open book. They'll be singing arias from Puccini's *Tosca* and telling thought-provoking jokes in the company of European royalty in some luxurious chalet up in the Swiss mountains, then they will be singing some common ballad and telling the most vulgar and banal jokes among a group of Russian businessmen at the bar of the Hotel Hermitage in Monaco. Put them in any crowd and they would be able to point out to you straight away who is loaded and who is not. And if you were to run into them at a supermarket, or while filling their tank with petrol at a gas station, they could easily come across as being surprisingly cranky and unpleasant. You see, entertainment for them is a profession not a hobby, and you cannot expect them to be working round the clock.

We had never been very close; he was an acquaintance rather than a friend. Yet he would call me now and again to invite me to various events. I guess he didn't mind showing up with a girl who was one third his age and who, most of the time, knew how to carry herself and looked the part. No, he didn't mind at all. He called me one afternoon saying that he had a very close friend in town, a Middle Eastern Prince, and he was wondering if I was interested in joining them for dinner at Annabel's. Was I interested? Not really, honestly! Who gives a shit about some Middle Eastern Prince? Well I certainly didn't.

To be quite frank with you, I never really thought too highly of filthy-rich Middle Easterners who, for the most part, valued women and pieces of furniture on equal terms. But I still went, as I really didn't have anything more stimulating to do that evening.

When I arrived at Annabel's I told the receptionist that I was there to join the Prince's table. After I checked in my coat and made sure that my make-up was still intact, I made my way to the dining area of the club. I was wearing a green sequined skirt, a gold top from Dolce & Gabbana and gold stilettos. I have to admit that I did look quite striking. That's what I like about Annabel's: it's definitely not the hippest venue in town, unless you like dancing to cheesy eighties tracks and rubbing shoulders with the jet-setting chichi crowd, but at least, as a girl, you can feed your exhibitionist streak and transform yourself into a glamorous diva for the night. Sometimes a girl just needs that.

As I approached the table three men stood up to greet me: the Lebanese, the Prince and his Personal Assistant. If nothing else, at least spending a few hours with three Middle Eastern men was going to do wonders for my self-esteem, I thought. An hour into our dinner, the P.A. was asking me for my address. I asked him what it was for and he replied, 'His Highness would like to send you a bouquet of roses.' I told him that I preferred that he didn't. By now, you must have become aware of my great enthusiasm for receiving a bouquet of flowers from a man. Yet the problem here wasn't my lack of interest in a bunch of roses, but the systematic and devious way that they were making their way to me. If a guy wants to send me flowers he does so by finding a way of discreetly obtaining my address; not by asking his P.A. to do the dirty work on his behalf. I also have to admit that I do find the way some Middle Eastern men act very quickly – making sure that they're not wasting any time with their prey and doing anything and everything in their power to seduce her – all very annoying and a little bit too presumptuous. Maybe if the Prince was a little more patient and at least made an effort to get to know me first, he would come to the conclusion that I wasn't the type of girl that was easily impressed by a stupid bouquet of roses.

Soon enough I would become aware that between the Prince and his P.A. there was a serious double act going on. You know, the good cop bad cop thing we so often come across in average Hollywood movies. The Prince was the highly well-mannered and polite one who knew never to cross the line. He always had a warm, pleasant smile on his face as he spoke of art, horseracing and the finer things in life that he had taken up to kill some of his precious time. He didn't have to necessarily flirt or show his keen interest in you, as it was the role of his P.A., or pimp to be more precise, who took the initiative in that particular department. Yet it wasn't as if he needed the extra help either as he was quite a good-looking, slim, very tall man in his mid-forties with dark skin, pitch black hair that he would always comb back, and a thin black moustache that gave him an overall nostalgic thirties look. Unlike most filthy rich Middle Easterns he had an immaculately refined dress sense. As he was very fond of horseracing, he owned a mansion in Goodwood where he would entertain his friends during the racing season. He was also very much married and had two grown up children.

Yet he would usually travel to Europe without his family; one couldn't help but wonder why.

He called me two weeks after that evening to say that he was coming to London soon and was to attend a black-tie private dinner party and was wondering if I would be interested in accompanying him. 'Yes, I would very much like that,' I had replied. Suddenly a part of me was taken by his title, his Middle Eastern background and the glamorous and privileged lifestyle that went hand-in-hand with it.

On the night of the dinner party his driver, who was a bald-headed, heavily built East Londoner with a strong cockney accent, came to pick me up with a latest edition black Bentley. As I was in the car I kept thinking, 'Here I am again, inside a Bentley. What is it with me and Bentleys?' I knew I wasn't going to get involved with him yet I have to admit that the whole set-up was very appealing. It wasn't only the fact that I still felt quite burnt-out after my previous experiences; but the thought of having an affair with a Middle Eastern prince seemed way too clichéd and out of my league. At the end of the day, I had no idea what these people were capable of and I didn't want to be a target in any way. I guess this must come as a surprise to you as I had not been so careful in the past, but for some reason, with the Prince, I strongly felt that I had to watch my back.

Then as the driver parked the car somewhere in Mayfair he told me that the Prince wanted to have a drink with me at his home before heading to the party. I said, 'Fine' as I really didn't have much of a choice. After he rang the doorbell for me, he slowly made his way back to the Bentley that was parked right in front of the house. In a matter of seconds I was greeted by one of the housekeepers who took me straight through to a massive living room with high ceilings, embellished with antique furniture, paintings and ornaments. It wasn't necessarily tasteful but it did look extravagant.

He asked me what I would like to drink to which I replied, 'Scotch whisky, very easy on the ice please.'

'The Prince will be with you very shortly.'

As I sat there examining the room, looking at the paintings that were hanging on the walls, which were mainly either large nineteenth-century landscape paintings or equestrian paintings, the silk Persian carpets on the floor and the Lalique and Dome glassware that was scattered everywhere, I really felt uncomfortable. My heart was racing and I wondered why. After all, he wasn't the first rich and powerful man that I had come into contact with in my life. Nor was it as if I had a crush on him. I guess it was his status rather than his wealth that made me feel so small and almost invisible seated there, taking a sip from my whisky now and again with my sweaty hands, trying to convince myself that it was not such a big deal after all.

Then he appeared with a big smile on his face and came up to me and gave me a warm kiss on both cheeks. As soon as he sat down the housekeeper reappeared and asked him what he would like to drink, and returned with a crystal glass of Chardonnay soon after. For about five minutes we made small talk and then, all of a sudden, one of his men showed up at the entrance of the living room with what appeared to be a wrapped up present and handed it to the Prince. He said as he passed it to me, 'I got you a small gift. I hope you will like it.'

I was lost for words as I started to unwrap it. I could feel the intense sensation from the blood rushing to my head; I knew I was seriously blushing as usual but there was nothing I could do about it. Then I opened the dark red velvet box and there it was, his small gift, a bracelet covered in diamonds and emeralds.

I said, 'It's beautiful but I cannot accept it.'

'Why is that?' he responded, with a surprised look on his face.

'Well, I hardly know you and it's anything but a small gift. It's too much.'

'Don't be silly. You don't know me yet but you'll soon find out that I am a man who loves to please his friends and you are a friend. It's as simple as that. Let me help you put it on.'

He was imposing his little gift on me and I was left with nothing to do but to thank him and wear it. He then said, while seated elegantly with his legs and hands crossed, 'So, you had told me that you were doing a master's degree, in Television Studies, if I remember correctly.'

'Yes, it's quite a stressful period for me,' I replied.

'And then, what do you intend to do once you've finished with your master's?'

'To get a job in Television, or Advertising or maybe even in PR. I am quite good with people so...'

'Well, I'm a highly connected person. Maybe I can help you. I know a lot of people in Hollywood. Have you ever considered becoming a movie star? You definitely have the looks for it.'

I smiled back at him shyly. 'Had I ever considered becoming a movie star?' I thought to myself. Well, in my fantasy world I had considered becoming just about everything including a movie star. At that instant I immediately pictured myself as the ambitious starlet who slept her way to the very top after being introduced to the Hollywood crowd by a powerful Middle Eastern Prince. The whole scenario made me feel sick. No, I didn't want to become a movie star; especially if my career depended on him. I looked back at him with an uneasy expression on my face.

'I just want to let you know that I will help you in any way I can. Such a stunning girl should never be concerned with money issues.'

While staring down at my glass of whisky I said, 'Thank you for your concern but I am sure I'll be fine. Actually I just got accepted as an intern at one of the leading advertising companies in the UK, so who knows?'

'Is that so? Well done.'

Then to change the subject, and to enable myself to forget the priceless bracelet I had on and therefore return to my natural colour, I said, 'You have a beautiful home.'

He replied, 'Thank you. We also have a very large garden and an indoor swimming pool.' He got up and made his way to the large set of windows overlooking his garden. I went to join him there and to continue our small talk, but my heart was still racing like mad. It was impossible to get over the bracelet and its implications; it was all I had on my mind. I looked out from the window and saw a large pond, adorned all around with flowers and trees. I said to him, 'It's great that you have a…well a…a small lake in your back garden.' I wanted to say pond but at that moment the word had suddenly disappeared from my vocabulary. I felt like a complete idiot next to this highly sophisticated man, a complete idiot who came across as not being able to tell the difference between a lake and a pond. Then out of the blue his P.A. appeared and he greeted me with a grin on his face. I was glad that he had come to my rescue. I seriously needed to lighten up.

Throughout dinner the P.A. was seated beside me and the Prince was seated across the table facing me. They continually played their double act as the P.A. would whisper in my ear how highly the Prince thought of me, how he really fancied me and how he had showed up in London earlier than planned just for me.

'His Highness has been talking only of you for the past two weeks. Seriously, I've never seen him like this before. It's as if you've cast a spell over him. But we really can't blame him, you really are a divine lady.'

I'd be lost for words as I looked across the table to see the Prince smiling warmly at me. If it wasn't for the bracelet I wouldn't have felt so repulsed and alarmed by what they were up to and would have even enjoyed the attention I was getting. Yet I could not help but feel extremely pressurized by the piece of jewellery I was forced to have. By accepting his gift had I, without having any control over the situation, put myself in a vulnerable position where I had to face the inevitable consequences? Was it really just a small gift for him or had we just signed a silent agreement that said a diamond/emerald-encrusted bracelet in return for a night of wild sex? Just the thought of it made me nauseous. If only he knew that he had a better chance of getting me into bed if he hadn't given me the bracelet in the first place.

Around midnight when most of the guests were still around and enjoying themselves I went up to the Prince and told him that I had to leave, that I had an early class the next day. I could tell that he was not too pleased about it but still smiled back at me and said, 'Next week I'm organizing a dinner at Harry's Bar and I will be attending a friend's black tie dinner party over the weekend in the country. I would love for you to join me.' I accepted as I felt that I didn't really have a choice while wearing his bracelet, or a solid excuse that I could come up with right there and then.

On my way out his P.A. came over and asked anxiously, 'Why are you leaving? We should not disappoint him. He really likes you and now he's going to feel rejected.'

What about how I felt and what I thought, did that have any relevance at all? I suppose not. I simply repeated the same scenario that I had previously done to the Prince as I was getting into the Bentley, and then took a deep breath as the car took off. Chatting with the driver on the way home felt like a breath of fresh air; he told me about his wife and how many children they had and that they were in the process of planning their next summer break somewhere in the south of Turkey.

The next day, sometime in the afternoon, while I was hooked in front of my computer, trying to work on a school project but instead going through the events of the previous night in my head continuously, I heard the doorbell ring. A minute later my landlady called out for me. She said that someone had dropped off a present for me. I quickly went down, grabbed it from her hands and without making a single remark took it upstairs with me. As I unwrapped the gift like a greedy little kid, I already knew exactly where it was coming from and what sort of a gift it was, yet as I opened the navy velvet angular box I was both repulsed and mesmerised by what was inside. A white gold Chopard "Ice Cube" model watch entirely paved with square-cut diamonds. Then the phone rang. I answered it; it was the Prince. Had I liked my little present? He had felt that he needed to thank me for accompanying him last night. I told him that it was beautiful but I could not possibly accept it. This time round, I tried to be firm with him but he just wouldn't take no for an answer.

'No, this is really too much for me. It makes me feel uncomfortable. I cannot...'

'This is just a little something to say thank you. It was so nice having you by my side last evening. Please don't take it the wrong way. And by the way, you are coming to the dinner I've organized at Harry's Bar and the dinner party at my friend's house in the country?' I sighed and then said, 'Well, yes, of course.'

Nevertheless literally after a day had gone by I felt under so much pressure that I could no longer breathe. I realised that I could not be a part of his games and, as it was impossible to make myself heard by him, I called his P.A. I said, 'Unfortunately, I have to turn down both invitations. I can't do this.'

He said, 'But why?'

'Well,' I replied, 'the Prince is a lovely man and I am very flattered that he is showing such keen interest in me. He has given me two priceless gifts and he's asking me to accompany him to a dinner and then a private house party, and all this is making me feel very uncomfortable. I want to return his gifts.'

He said that the Prince would never accept something like that, what is given could never be taken back; it would go against his ethics. Well, it was good to know that he had some, I thought. He tried to persuade me to go back on my decision but I told him that I had made up my mind. He said, 'Well, why don't you tell him yourself?' I said that it was better that he do it for me. Then I hung up, feeling relieved knowing that a serious weight had been lifted from my shoulders and that I could go on with my life as usual. I took the bracelet and the watch out of their boxes and inspected them closely as I was lying in bed. Now that I had removed all the implications I could finally enjoy them for what they were. I even arranged to meet a friend at the bar of Blakes Hotel for a drink that night in order to wear my new diamond-encrusted watch.

At a quarter to nine in the evening, as I was walking to the hotel, my phone rang. I picked up; it was the Prince. I guess it wasn't going to be so easy to put everything behind me after all. He said, 'My P.A. told me everything. You have totally misunderstood me. I gave you those two gifts because you are a very attractive, smart girl and I really love having you around. You should never feel any sort of pressure with me. Just because I gave you two small gifts doesn't mean that I expect anything in return. I am a rich man and I can afford to spoil my friends. I would love for you to turn up to both of the dinners that I will be attending next week, as a friend. It would make me very happy to see you there and I can give you my word that you'll never be put in a position that will make you feel uncomfortable.' Well, what can I say, he was making a serious effort here and although I doubted that he was sincere, and that it wasn't yet another tactic of his to draw me into his web, I still felt that after all that he had said I could not turn him down again.

The following week, on Wednesday evening, his driver came to pick me up and take me to Harry's Bar in Mayfair. Surprisingly I was the first guest to arrive. As I sat there beside him at the bar of this very exclusive restaurant, he started chatting to me about horseracing, the horses he owned and how passionate he was about it and so on. I wasn't really listening; I was in a rather existential state of mind. I don't know why. Maybe it was because I could not care less about some dull elitist hobby a rich Prince was bragging on about. Or maybe it was simply the fact that I had no compatibility on any level with this man who was so keen on making some sort of an impression on me. Then he said that he was looking forward to introducing a friend of his to me. I was going to meet him on Saturday at his family home in the country where they were organizing a dinner party for the Prince. He was a great guy with a very sharp English sense of humour; I was going to adore him. He said, 'Especially when he gets a bit tipsy and starts going up and down to his cellar to bring out some more of his wine. He becomes so hilarious. You just have to see him. Well, you'll understand just what I mean when you meet him this Saturday.' Then just to keep the conversation flowing I asked him about his kids and his wife and he told me that although he loved his kids he was very unhappy in his marriage. Actually he was seriously thinking of a divorce. Then his guests started to arrive.

By the time we were all seated at a large round table we were around twelve people. Some I had met previously at other boring dinner parties and others I was meeting for the first time. It turned out to be an uneventful evening and the Prince's driver dropped me home, around midnight. Though I did have a slightly embarrassing experience during dinner. The Prince was sitting across the table from me and as I looked at him now and again he would smile at me and naturally I would smile back at him. At one point I excused myself to go to the rest-room and as I was washing my hands, this stunning black girl who was also seated at our table came in. While we were both applying our lipstick she said that she had to tell me something. I said, 'What is it?' 'Well,' she said, 'you have a piece of spinach between your teeth.' I guess she had noticed it while the Prince and I had been smiling back and forth at each other. I looked at the mirror to examine my teeth and there it was, a huge chunk of spinach covering an entire front tooth, creating the illusion of a wide empty gap between the neighbouring teeth. Maybe that's why he had been smiling continuously at me. Maybe he had found it amusing to look at a girl who had spent hours in front of the mirror to prepare herself for the night, only to be thwarted by a piece of spinach. Well, that's life for you.

The following Saturday, around 7 pm, I was in a helicopter heading for a country house with two other guests and the P.A. Throughout our half-hour journey I hid behind an open magazine that I wasn't reading in order to avoid looking down and making everybody aware of my phobia. When we finally landed, got off the helicopter and made our way across the crisp green lawn, we were greeted by the hosts, a British husband and wife in their late fifties who had spent months organizing this particular night just to amuse their Middle Eastern friend who had been financially supporting the racing horses they were devotedly breeding in the stables next to their lavish country house. One of the housekeepers took the Louis Vuitton weekend bag that I was carrying and said that she was going to put it away in my room. Yes, like the Prince, I was to stay there for the night, but he had reassured me that I was to have my very own separate bedroom.

When the twenty-one guests were eventually seated at the large oval table which was embellished with flowers, candles, silverware and fine china, I turned round to the man who was seated on my left as he asked me where I was from and where I was living.

After answering his questions and in order to keep the conversation flowing I said, 'Whereabouts are you from? Do you live around here?'

He replied with an annoyed look on his face and said, 'This is my home, I live here.'

At that moment, it hit me that he had made himself known to me literally not more than an hour ago when I had first arrived there. Actually he and his wife were the first two people that I had been introduced to yet, ironically, I seemed to have no recollection of their faces or their names whatsoever. Whether it was the after-effect of the nerve-racking helicopter journey or just simply because I couldn't care less, or even the re-appearance of my old-time friend, the semi-transparent shield, I had totally forgotten about our initial encounter. All I could remember was meeting a faceless couple. Nevertheless, the bottom line is, it was embarrassing and he didn't seem to be too impressed by my ignorance either and made it clear throughout dinner and for the rest of the night by making sarcastic remarks at anything I had to say or do. After dinner, when I ran in to him just as he was coming out of his cellar with a bottle of red wine, he gave me a dirty old man's look. His eyes wandered up and down my entire body and finally became fixed on my cleavage. He said in a belittling manner, 'So, how is the Turkish Delight doing? I just love Turkish Delights, they are my favourite.' Yes, I had made a little mistake, but come on! He didn't have to rub it in my face the whole night long. But he did and when I woke up the next day at around seven o'clock, I quickly got up, prepared myself, found the Prince's driver and asked him to take me back to London before anyone else, and especially the host, got up.

I don't know whether it was his unpleasant remarks or the whole unwelcoming, stiff atmosphere created by the majority of people there, who were rich, upper-class, public-school educated Brits; but for me the night had been anything but entertaining. Especially during dinner, when the Prince had stood up at one point to make a speech and thank his lovely friend and his wife for going to so much trouble for him, organizing such a lovely dinner party and bringing together such a wonderful group of people. I could not help but wonder whether any of these middle-aged, upper-class snobs (who, for some reason, reminded me of the stereotypical, greedy patronizing British imperialists that you so often come across in war movies) would even bother to associate themselves with a middle-eastern if it wasn't for the big chunk of money he was providing for the maintenance of their horses? The answer is simply no.

After that evening I was never to see the Prince again. He

did though call me up on various occasions when he was back in town again, briefly, to invite me to a party or a dinner but I would turn down his invitations each time by saying that I was busy or going away to Istanbul. The four separate evenings that I had spent in his company and with his friends had made me realise that I wasn't having fun with him or his crowd. So there was no point in continuing to torture myself.

It was some time in July, when I had started working as an intern at the advertising agency, that a girlfriend of mine called me up to give me the bad news: the Prince had died of a heart attack at his palace in his home town. I couldn't believe my ears. Was I like a shitty version of a black widow where the rich and powerful men I came into contact with died before I got even close to marrying them (although I had no intention of doing so, but would probably have given it a second thought if I had known that they would cease to exist in a matter of a few months).

I guess it's plain human psychology that one only remembers the good aspects of a person that has just passed away. The Prince was a generous, kind-natured, sophisticated man who had always been a gentleman towards me and I had been avoiding him for the past month and now he was dead; I really felt guilty. I had to do something about it so I called his home in London, his homes in Goodwood and in his homeland hoping that I could speak to his P.A. and explain how sorry I was, but it was impossible to get through to him so I just left messages with whoever answered the phone by giving them my name and tried to explain to them how shattered I was by the incident.

A month later I was in Istanbul on a warm summer evening, all dressed up, going out of my Mother's apartment when my mobile rang. I picked it up. It was a woman who spoke with a very heavy Arabic accent. She said, 'How much do you charge men you disgusting fucking whore?'

I thought of hanging up but I was curious to find out who on earth it was so I asked, 'Who is this?'

She said, 'Tell me how much you charge men you piece of fucking stinking shit? What is your price for the night? Women like you make me sick!'

Words are not enough to describe the intense hatred that was accelerating from her voice. I told her that I had no idea what she was going on about and then added, 'You have to help me here, there must be some misunderstanding as I'm definitely not in that profession. Is this about a man?'

She replied, 'Yes, it's about a man who has recently died.'

I said, 'Then it must be about the Prince.'

'Correct,' she replied and then I continued, 'Of course I know the Prince, I mean I knew. It is really sad that he died, he was a lovely man.'

I guess our thoughts weren't mutual as she replied, 'No, he was a cold-hearted pig who deserved to die!'

'Who are you?' I asked.

She said, 'I am one of you.'

I told her that although I had been in the company of the Prince on several occasions and that he had been keen on me, nothing had happened between us.

Then she said, 'What about the diamond-emerald bracelet and the diamond-encrusted Chopard watch? Is that how he paid for your services?'

As soon as she mentioned the bracelet and the watch I just panicked and told her that I had never received such gifts from him. I felt that if I were to confirm that he had given me such priceless gifts, it would be more difficult to convince her that nothing had happened between us, yet it was stupid, as she somehow already knew about them.

Then she said, 'You better watch your back. Very bad things are going to happen to you. I am going to make you feel sorry that you ever lived. Just wait and see.' Then she hung up.

Who could it be? I thought to myself. Well, it must be his wife but still, why would she call me and threaten me like that even if I had had an affair with him? The guy was dead, what difference would it make? A few close friends said that maybe I was in his Will and was now a rich woman. I told them that although the whole scenario was very appealing, why would a man put someone in his Will after merely meeting up with them on four different occasions? I had been just an acquaintance not a girl he had a mad, passionate love affair with. I am sure he had a long list of mistresses who were more suitable for the role.

During my month-long vacation with friends there were times in open-air clubs in Istanbul, or at a friend's yacht near Bodrum, when the whole incident would flash through my mind and would make me shiver for a moment. I wondered if she really meant what she said, but then I would try to dismiss it as some crazy widow's irrational behaviour right after her husband's death.

The day I returned to London and my landlady opened the front door for me I asked her if everything had been okay while I was away. She said everything was fine but she had received two peculiar phone calls in connection with me. She said, 'The first one was from a flower shop. They said that they had an order for you and wanted the exact date of your return and they were quite persistent to find out. The second one was from a railway station in Manchester. They said they had found some luggage with your name and address on the tag and asked all sorts of questions about you. I found it all a bit odd. By the way, I am going away to Spain for a week's holiday tomorrow.' I tried to act calmly so as to not alarm her and went quietly upstairs to my bedroom.

Immediately after, I called the Lebanese and told him briefly what had happened over the phone to which he said, 'We have to meet up.' I told him that we could get together in a few days' time but he replied, 'We need to meet as soon as possible.' So we met on that very same night at the bar at Blakes Hotel. He asked me to go over every single little detail about the Prince, like how many times I had met up with him, how keen had he been on me and so on. The Lebanese suggested that maybe his intentions had been much more than I had thought them to be. After all I was a well-educated Muslim girl with a good background, maybe he saw me as his future wife? Maybe during an argument with his wife he had mentioned the young Turkish girl he was planning to leave her for? I was highly impressed by his imagination but was well aware that the only plan the Prince had for me was to get me between the sheets and nothing more. Then he said, 'You know there is a big mystery surrounding his death. He wanted to divorce his wife and there is a rumour going round that says she killed him. Nobody knows for sure that it was a heart attack.' I asked him if he had ever met her and he replied, 'Yes on a number of occasions. She always came across as a very unstable woman. You have to seriously watch yourself. She can be very dangerous and she has the financial backup to go after you and harm you. These people are so fucked up, she can have someone throw nitric acid on your face and you'd be scarred for life. I suggest you change your phone number, your address and never talk to anyone who is in any way related to the Prince. Well, apart from me.' That was the only time I was to ever see him or talk to him again.

After he dropped me home that night, I called my mobile phone company to change my number. The woman on the end of the line asked me why I wanted to change it. I told her the whole story as I strongly felt that I had to share it with someone, anyone. She said that it was a terrible thing and that I ought to go to the police, then put me on hold. As I was waiting on hold I kept telling myself that maybe all that the Princess wanted to do was to frighten me just for the hell of it but what if...what if it was more than that and her men were already on their way heading towards my house with the nitric acid, or a silent gun? I quickly went to my bedroom door and opened it halfway. The rest of the house was pitch-black, my landlady had turned all the lights out and had already gone to bed. I shut the door and locked it firmly. I turned off the light in my room and was now sitting on my bed in complete darkness.

When the phone operator came back on line, feeling that I

was not alone after all, I got up and switched on the light again. She said, 'According to our records, in the past two weeks someone has been continuously calling us and has been for some reason trying to get into your account. Let me see…yes they have called us twenty-one times. The last call was made yesterday morning.' I switched off the light again. At this stage I was shaking all over as I asked her, 'Well, were they able to?' She replied 'No, they didn't know all your details like your date of birth and your Mother's maiden name. This all sounds very scary but I have changed your number and I hope that you'll be fine.' After I switched on the light again, I thanked her and hung up.

I stood still for a moment and then switched off the light one more time and went next to the window to see what was going on outside. I could almost imagine a red light right on the middle of my forehead. Maybe these people could see me in complete darkness with the special headgear they had on? I quickly took a step back. Why was this happening to me? I hadn't done anything wrong. Maybe God was making me pay for all my past sins? Let's face it: I hadn't been a complete saint so far. Remember, the two abortions, the affair with a married man and stealing food, to name but a few? Yes, my great enthusiasm for adventure had finally kicked me right in the ass when I had least expected it. Now I had turned my life into a complete Hollywood thriller; yet unlike most Hollywood thrillers I had no idea how this was all going to end.

I had to pee but was too scared to go the bathroom which was literally next door. First I drew the curtains and then I switched on the lamp by my bed. You see staying in complete darkness was a safer option yet it also scared the hell out of me, so I had to find middle ground. I then quietly unlocked my bedroom door and switched on the corridor light, went into the bathroom and peed with the door open. Even my urine was too frightened to come out as it sizzled weakly down the toilet. When I had finished, I took an empty washbowl that was lying on the floor of the bathroom, switched off the corridor light, tiptoed quickly back into my bedroom and locked the door. My heart was racing like mad. At least I no longer needed to go through the same ordeal each time I had to pee during the night.

When I did wake up the next day, with a stinking bowl full of urine right in the middle of my bedroom – which I have to admit was disgusting, revolting, you name it – the intensity of my fear had somehow disappeared, as if it had all been nothing but a bad dream. I went downstairs to prepare myself some breakfast. It was an old, three-storey Victorian house. The kitchen and the living room were on the ground floor, my landlady's bedroom, bathroom and study room on the first floor, and my bedroom and bathroom were on the top floor. There was also a large garden in the back and no, we didn't have a security alarm system. I was just about to dive into a bowl of muesli when I heard my landlady's footsteps as she was coming down the stairs. It had totally slipped my mind that she was off to Spain that day, leaving me in this house of suspense all by myself. I had always felt uneasy being left here on my own whenever she went away. Chelsea is one of the safest neighbourhoods in London but still to be all alone in this unguarded old house never made me feel at ease. As she said goodbye to me and made her way out of the house with her small suitcase, I realised that there was no way I was going to stay there for another night. So, I called one of my closest friends, a Turkish woman in her mid-thirties who owned a restaurant in Soho. She had been married to a Tunisian guy for the past five years and was at that time eight and a half months pregnant. When I explained to her what was going on she told me that I was welcome to stay at her place for a little while, until I found a place of my own. I was surprised, as I, for sure, would not want someone in my circumstances staying at my place. I guess the fact that she was married to a drug addict who would disappear sometimes for three nights in a row also seemed to help. As she was in the late stages of her pregnancy, she needed a friend by her side.

I quickly went upstairs and packed what I could; I was going to get the rest of my stuff later on. As I packed two large suitcases in complete silence, listening to every crack, hum and any sort of noise coming from God knows where, I was shivering with fear and my heart was again racing. Then the doorbell rang. I froze. I certainly wasn't going to answer it but I couldn't help but wonder who the hell it could possibly be. If they were here to get me, would they be polite enough to ring the doorbell? Well, an easy access would be very handy. After standing still for about a minute or so I took the house keys and slowly made my way down the narrow creaky wooden staircase. You know, when you're watching a typical Hollywood horror movie and you simply can't understand why the heroine goes downstairs to answer the door, even though she suspects that it might be the serial killer who's out to get her; well, let me point out to you that those scenes are not so unrealistic after all. Regardless of the immensity of your fears you come to the conclusion that it's better to face them than to feel like a trapped victim, who's waiting for her killer. At least by going downstairs I felt that I had a better chance of escaping, unless I was willing to jump out of a three-storey building,

I went into the living room and looked through the gap between the curtains. No, there was no longer anyone standing in front of the house, but there were a few people walking about in the street. One was putting money into the parking meter across the road, another was walking towards the end of the street, en route for Fulham Road, another one was getting into his car. I watched all three of them until they disappeared. Soon I realised that I had a seriously difficult task to accomplish as more and more people were making their way into our street. Till that day I had never noticed that I was living in one of the busiest streets in Chelsea. It was impossible to keep track of each and every person. As I was looking at the guy who was walking his dog, making sure that there wasn't anything peculiar about his behaviour, I had totally lost the lead on the woman who had just parked her car. After realising my efforts were pointless and bordering on paranoia, I went upstairs to finish with my packing.

When I had made my way quickly to the end of the road and onto Fulham Road with two bulging suitcases, that for some reason I had no problem carrying at all, I waited eagerly for a cab. I looked around me; the road was busy with people and cars coming from all sorts of directions. I felt completely naked, like being surrounded by a group of hungry wolves, without even a rifle to defend myself. Everything seemed sharper than ever; colours were brighter, the car engines and voices of people were louder, and the speed of the cars and the people that were passing by me were faster than ever. All my senses were alert, trying to pick up every single detail around me all at once. I felt dizzy. Then I saw an empty cab and made a signal. The driver stopped right in front of me and lowered his window; I stared at him for a second and then said, 'To St. John's Wood please.'

Once I was in the car, I jumped at the clicking sound of the central lock system. What if the driver was one of them and I was locked inside a cab heading to my torture chamber or deathbed? I tried to open the window on my right and after a few abrupt unsuccessful attempts with my sweaty hands, finally managed it. Okay, here was the plan: I would carefully monitor the route that he was going to take to St. John's Wood, and as soon as I realised that he wasn't going the right way I would jump out of the window at the first set of lights. I had to bid farewell to some of my favourite outfits but under the circumstances, it wasn't such a high price to pay. Yet, just as we were passing through Marylebone Road, I calmed down and persuaded myself that I was not being kidnapped by a fifty-something-year-old East Londoner. By that time not only was I certain that he was taking the right route, but also that it would be mighty hard for them to arrange a cab driver to kidnap me at such short notice. Well, unless they had bugged my phone and had hired a Turkish translator to eavesdrop on the phone conversation that I had with the Restaurant Owner. No, come on, I was going way too far. But was I really? Okay, being suspicious of this particular cab driver was seriously pushing it a bit too far, yet my fear of being kidnapped, tortured, raped and even murdered was still a real issue. The difficulty with the whole set-up was that, although I had been made aware that I had a new enemy, I had no clue whatsoever as to what extent she was actually going to pursue her mission to take revenge. What if she really did have me murdered or turned me into a faceless being where I had to go through fifty operations just to have my nose back, wouldn't that be a bit unfair? Considering the amount of injustice in the world, I would probably be just another misunderstood victim that had made the stupid mistake of being in the wrong place at the wrong time. It was as simple as that.

I felt somewhat more at ease in the two-bedroom flat my friend owned in a large apartment block, as we lay down on two separate sofas in the living room and watched a series of *Friends* and then *Frasier.* The fear was still there but my friend's laidback attitude towards life had lessened its intensity. I guess it was the only way she had been able to deal with her drug-addict husband for so long. Yet, the big challenge was awaiting me the following day: I was to attend the final term of my master's degree.

I went to school the next day, walking as fast as I could with my head facing down. I only looked up when I felt someone approaching me, or to check if anyone had been following me. Midway, a tall Middle Eastern guy came up to me to ask for directions and what did I do? I ran as fast as I could until I was certain that he had lost my track. Yes, in just two days I had transformed into a paranoid freak, and I was aware that my behavioural pattern was pushing the limits of sanity but I simply wasn't mentally equipped to handle the situation. I considered the number of times I had been tested for HIV (four times in three years), the sleepless nights I had had due to my fear of being diagnosed with lung cancer after smoking more than a packet of cigarettes earlier that day, the nights spent in bed promising myself that I would go to a warehouse store the next day to get a few meters of rope that I could use in case a fire broke out at our house and I had to escape through the window, and my phobia of flying: paranoia was already in me, peeking out whenever it had the chance. Now it had taken over my intellect, my emotions, my body, in fact my whole existence.

In class, as the tutor was mumbling some words that I could not possibly make any sense of, and flicking through some slides that were way too bright to look at, I was struggling to breathe. What was the point of all this? Why was I there when I could be dead tomorrow? And who were all these people? I looked at the faces of each and every one of them, it was pitch dark but I could tell who was who. But did I really know who was who? I had been studying with them for the past year, but to me they were still complete strangers. Suddenly I felt this intense feeling of hatred towards all of them. I was jealous. Maybe they had worries of their own like an aching heart after a break-up, or a stingy Father who never gave them sufficient pocket money, but at least they didn't have some mad Princess chasing after them. I got up and left the classroom.

A week had gone by when I decided to transfer my studies to a university in Istanbul. I was finally done with London. It was no longer a vibrant city that offered endless opportunities, but a massive whirlpool of filth and corruption that was eagerly waiting to swallow you. I forced myself to see the positive aspects of the city I had been dreading to return to for the past five years. But as my fear of facing up to my past had been replaced by a much stronger force it wasn't so difficult to persuade myself that I was ready, once more, to make Istanbul my new home.

With its ecstatic beauty, pulsating energy, diverse cultural heritage, Istanbul is a city that has its very own smell and flavour, which you cannot help but crave from time to time. And to be quite frank with you, even to this day, I still sit back and light a cigarette whenever I pass over the Bosphorus Bridge and gaze out of the window with fascination at the breathtaking beauty this ancient city has to offer. As for its people? Yes, we Turks can sometimes be liars and back-stabbers yet at the same time we are warm-hearted, hospitable, passionate and courageous beings.

Whenever I walk through the streets of Istanbul and feel repulsed by the sexually frustrated men who whistle at me or whisper, just enough for me to hear, that I have an amazing ass that they would love to get their dirty hands on, I am also well aware that these men would instantly run to my rescue if I was ever under any kind of serious threat. In Turkey, people stand up for one another and take care of each other regardless of who you are; even if you are a total stranger walking in the middle of the night through a dark alleyway, or a neighbour who desperately needs some medication for her sick child at four in the morning. If you have a problem, people don't just shrug their shoulders like they do in London and say it's not any of their business, they genuinely try to help in any way they can, because they care and because they don't have the heart to stand and watch someone who is in desperate need. Well, that's just us Turks for you; temperamental, unreliable and narrow-minded, yet a nation of good Samaritans.

I contacted a few universities that offered a Television Studies-related master's programme in Istanbul. Unfortunately I was rejected by every single one of them on the grounds that I was too late with my application. Fucking Turkish bureaucracy. I guess it was fate really. London had become my home, I was destined to stay, whether I liked it or not. And to be honest with you, although, still to this day, I sometimes bitch about London, as one inevitably does about a loved one, I know deep down inside that it's too late for us to part, there are so many heartaches and joys that we've shared together; London and I have become inseparable. For the first time in my life I truly believe that I belong somewhere. I might be a Turk by origin but more importantly I feel that I am a Londoner by choice. Whenever I arrive at Heathrow Airport from god knows where, I sigh and feel relieved that I am finally home. That's so important for me.

Six weeks had gone by and I started to lighten up a bit. Well, I did once go to the head of our department, who was an English guy in his early fifties with a serious dandruff problem, and cried my eyes out till he came over and gave me a pat on the shoulder. I guess he found the whole thing rather intriguing and was somewhat glad that not all his students spent their time away from school getting trashed in some local pub. No, there definitely was more to a student's life in London if you played your cards wrong. I spent all of my nights lying on a sofa, with the pregnant Restaurant Owner and watching the Paramount Comedy Channel while munching hotdogs or Chinese take-aways. Peculiar as it may sound, for some reason her uncontrollable food cravings had passed onto me. I would call her on my way from school every day so as to come to a mutual agreement on what we should be having for dinner that night. Sometimes her husband would appear out of the blue. Becoming fully aware that there was no room left for him, as we had taken up the two large sofas in the small living room, he would either go to their bedroom and crash for a couple of hours to recharge his batteries, or just pick up something and leave soon after.

I had always despised her husband; it was impossible not to. He was a filthy scumbag who preferred to leave his pregnant wife for days on end, just to get high on some coke and god knows what else he was hooked on. Whenever I saw him I would simply say, 'Hi, how are you?' but nothing more, just to be polite to *her.* If it wasn't for her, I would never bother to make that much of an effort to the lying, stealing son of a bitch that he was. She would always remind me to watch my purse whenever he dropped by. Why she would still have him around, to this day I have never understood.

Then one evening when I was fast asleep in the guest room, right in the middle of a dream, I felt someone getting into my bed. I wasn't quite sure whether it was part of my dream or that it was happening for real. Yet as he started to make his way towards me, snuggling up closer and closer, I felt obliged to wake myself up and make some sense of what was going on. As I slowly lifted my heavy eyelids there he was right beside me, pretending to be fast asleep. You see, words are not enough to describe the hatred I feel towards him and his kind. People like him like to play it stupid, as if they are somehow always misunderstood. They are such professional liars that they deny every accusation that they are faced with even if you catch them in the act. They treat you as a complete retard and even if you are one hundred per cent sure that they are full of shit, they still get away with it and it's so fucking annoying. It's not what they say but the way they say it, that makes it all work. They simply look into your eyes, and without a blink of an eyelid come up with such unconvincing excuses that they switch roles with you and actually become the innocent and misinterpreted party and you are left speechless. Such people can seriously drive you insane so it's best to just stay away from them, because with them you can never win. I jumped out of the bed and whispered, 'What the hell do you think you are doing?' He woke up from his pretend sleep and said that he didn't know what he was doing there either and that he must have been sleep walking. 'Yeah, right,' I thought. Yet I didn't want to make a big scene as I assumed that that was the last thing my friend needed right now, as she was fast asleep in the room next door, carrying his child. I switched on the light and said, 'I will only say this once. You are never, but never to come into my room ever again. Do you understand me?' He nodded. 'Fine, just get the hell out of here,' I added. Then he left, but at least I was sure that he wouldn't dare do it again.

Unfortunately I was wrong. Only a week had gone by when

I was again asleep in bed and I suddenly opened my eyes to see him standing in front of me, just staring at me while holding up my duvet. As soon as he realised that he had woken me up he took a step back and said, 'Shit!' I got up and whispered, 'You fucking son of a bitch. What the hell do you think you are doing?' He told me that we had to be quiet so as to not wake up his wife and that I had totally misunderstood him. He said, 'I just needed a friend to talk to. I feel so lonely and my wife keeps shutting me out, treating me like I don't exist; I was hoping that we could talk a little.' 'At five o'clock in the morning?' I demanded. After using up my not-so-extensive vocabulary of insults and swearwords on him, he started to sob. How low could he get? He obviously didn't have any set parameters.

At that moment I knew that I could no longer stay with them. So I started looking for a new home. When I told the Restaurant Owner that I was moving into a flat in Notting Hill to live with a newly divorced Serbian woman in her late thirties and her eight-year-old daughter, naturally she was upset to be left all on her own and tried to persuade me to stay a bit longer but I had already made up my mind.

Being a high risk-taker in life, whether it involved hitch-hiking in the streets of Istanbul or sleeping over at a complete stranger's house with the hope of not getting raped, has inevitably made me place great emphasis on the human gaze. I think those first few moments of eye contact with a person are crucial in deciphering whether or not he or she has some very twisted hidden traits. Do they look you straight in the eyes, or are they checking you out from head to toe, or do they avoid looking at you in the face at all as they speak? I find it reassuring if a person looks directly into my eyes yet if their look turns into a disturbing stare I come to the conclusion that I am in fact in the company of a sex maniac. Whereas if a person is doing the opposite, that is, avoiding looking me straight in the eye while making all these tense and abrupt gestures with their sweaty hands, I can easily picture myself in their crummy little flat all tied up, just waiting my turn to be made into a main course. When I came into contact with the Serbian Woman for the first time, the moment she opened the front door to her flat, I noticed that she had checked me out from head to toe with a disturbing, insincere, cool expression on her face, which I would normally have found alarming. Yet at that stage, out of mere desperation, I chose not to dwell on it too much but instead tried to focus on whether there was enough space in the flat for the excessive amount of clothing that I had. After asking if she had any house rules that I needed to know about to which she replied, 'No' with a dull expression on her face, I told her that I could move in the next day, provided that it was all right with her. She nodded.

When I left her flat I took a long stroll around my new neighbourhood. I was quite excited about moving to Notting Hill; it was the coolest area in town, very bohemian chic, yes definitely very me or at least what I had just suddenly aspired to become that day. I started imagining how my life was going to transform once I moved there. I was going to hang out with the arty-farty crowd: musicians, film directors, artists and actors, yet I needed to buy a few extra items for my wardrobe. I had to somehow transform my Eurotrash image; maybe by getting some new pieces from a second hand shop, or even better, getting some antique kaftans on my next trip to Istanbul. When there is a will there is always a way. At the weekends I could hang around Portobello Market and maybe even start collecting antique stuff. Actually, I could take up painting again, and spend my free time painting while listening to improvisational jazz. Hang on a minute. Didn't I used to compose songs when I was around twelve? I tried to remember the lyrics to one of my songs:

> People are all the same,
> They give me pain
> Well it's hard to explain
> People are the same
> I don't want to complain
> But they'd do anything for fame
> I don't know which world to live in
> I don't know which person to believe in
> All I want is a world of my own
> A world which is always unknown
> 'Cause people are all the same...

What a depressing song for a kid to compose. I was a frustrated artist even before I knew it. Who knows? Maybe I could end up being a Renaissance woman, a woman of the arts. Even if my artistic capabilities don't bear fruit in great masterworks that will stand as milestones in the realm of the arts, I could always end up being an artist's muse or something. As long as I don't have to pose with my bra off that is. I hate my breasts...

I could just picture myself wearing a worn-down old Ottoman kaftan over a pair of faded jeans and a plain black polo-neck jumper, with messy hair while puffing away at a cigarette with my hands covered in dry paint, making my way to a coffee shop to meet up with my similarly gifted friends. Then of course I would have my equally bohemian boyfriend. I tried to picture how I would like my future boyfriend to be. If I was going to become bohemian I had to embrace it with every inch of my existence and go all the way. He had to be young and extremely sexy, rough instead of polished and possibly the son of a Lord who liked to play down his privileged background by living in some small run-down flat in Notting Hill. At least then, whenever we got bored with the whole bohemian thing, we could go over to his parent's huge mansion in the countryside and live a little. And bohemian is always good. Okay, you naturally have the risk of fucking up your liver with the heavy amount of drinking and smoking that is involved with the image, but at least you have *the world on a string, sitting on a rainbow, got the world wrapped around your finger*[15], or at least that's how you might think.

There was only one slight problem with the whole scenario and that was the Serbian Woman. Well, to put it frankly, she didn't quite fit in with the whole bohemian scenario. She was a gigantically tall and muscular woman who both dressed and looked like a peasant. She belonged more on a farm where she would wake up early every morning to milk the cows with her strong bare hands, than the arty scene of Notting Hill. Yet

15 This line is an extract from an old jazz number *I've Got the World on a String* (words by Ted Koehler & music by Harold Arlen)

looking back at it now, the problem was not about the way she looked but how she came across as a person. I guess, at the time, I was too scared to face my true instincts about her.

The day I moved in I was hanging my clothes onto the rails while smoking a cigarette and I heard a knock on my door. I said, 'Yes?' She asked me if she could come in, to which I replied, 'Sure.' As she came in, she took a quick glance at the room and said with a frozen grin on her face, 'I forgot to tell you yesterday, I don't allow smoking in the flat. You see, I used to be a smoker myself but I quit a year ago so I would really appreciate if you didn't smoke.' I totally accept the fact that smoking is one of the worst addictions in the world, yet you need to be fully aware that a smoker can only put an end to her/his horrible substance abuse in her/his own time. Just as you cannot expect a coke addict to stop snorting right there and then, you can't expect the same from a smoker either. As a smoker you have to mentally prepare and brainwash yourself for a fair amount of time with how great your life is going to be once you stop smoking before you actually do. Just as I was getting to transform myself to my new bohemian image she had made her first act of sabotage by asking me to quit smoking. A bohemian that doesn't smoke? You must be joking! I said, 'You didn't mention anything about smoking yesterday when I asked you if there were any house rules.' Well it had just slipped out of her mind. I told her that I could cut down a little, and only smoke in my room with the door shut and the windows wide open, and go outside occasionally to smoke as well, but to actually give it up, sadly it wasn't going to happen overnight. She wasn't too happy with my response but I was just being honest with her.

Too soon I was to find out that I was sharing a flat with a highly unstable and problematic woman who just couldn't get over the fact that her English husband had left her for someone else. Whereas I couldn't understand why he had married her in the first place. She played the role as a wife and Mother who had been abandoned by her horrible husband ever so well in front of her daughter only too often. Whenever her daughter asked her what was wrong and why she looked so sad she would reply to the little girl, 'Because your daddy left me and ran off with another woman. He doesn't care about us any longer. He's not giving us enough money either. He's making us starve here. Your Father is an extremely selfish man.' The poor guy had already given up his flat to her and was sending her a monthly allowance, what more did she want? Maybe instead of sitting aimlessly on her fat ass all day, if she got a job instead and stopped dwelling on how horrible her ex-husband was, we could all take a deep breath and enjoy life a little. Yet I tried to be nice to her. I even gave her my Hermès perfume that smelled like some heavy, spicy Middle-Eastern cologne, which I had bought by mistake at a duty free shop. Yet I knew that I would never be able to charm her by being nice to her. Of course she had every right to feel let down by her husband, yet that did not justify the way she made everyone around her miserable; especially her pretty little girl. How was her daughter ever going to grow into a mature and confident woman when she was reminded on a daily basis that her Father didn't love her?

As I was on my way out one morning, heading to school, she asked if she could have a word with me. She was sitting in the tastelessly decorated, nearly empty large living room that only had two sofas and a television set. I went in to join her. She said, 'Why do you sleep so late?' I told her I that I was studying. 'Well, I believe that it's healthier to study during the day. Why don't you try doing that?' she suggested. I told her that I preferred to study in the night. Then she said, 'I was just thinking of your wellbeing. It's not good to be up till one o'clock at night, plus I might have to charge you extra for the electricity once the bill arrives.' I just said, 'Fine' and then left. Although my previous Argentinian landlady wasn't a particularly friendly woman, at least she would mind her own business. I remember the nights I would turn up at home at two o'clock in the morning drunk as a fish after a dull night at Tramp where I had spent the whole night sitting down and never getting up even once to dance. I would go up to my bedroom, put my Barry White CD on with the headphones and dance naked till the early hours in the morning. Those were the days...

So a few days later when she barged into my room while I was asleep, around two in the morning, yelling like some psycho-maniac because I had left my bathroom light on, I realised that I was fed up with being constantly on the run from firstly a lunatic widow, then a pervert husband and finally a mad divorcee. What was the matter with all of these people and what did they want from me? No, I was not going to take any more shit from anyone; I wanted my life back and I had no intention of taking another chance with a complete stranger so I called my Argentinian landlady the next day and told her that I wanted to move back in. There I had freedom to do as I pleased and that, for me, was way more important than anything else life had to offer.

9

The Love of My Life

I said, as we were sitting at a candle-lit table having dinner, overlooking the Bosphorus at Korfez Restaurant, 'Just say it and let's get it over and done with.'

He asked me for a cigarette. I gave him one knowing that his doctor had firmly told him to quit. Though at this point there were larger issues at stake; even larger than his health. After lighting the cigarette with the candle, which some believe is bad luck, he looked straight into my eyes and simply said with utter seriousness, 'You know what you are? You are nothing but a stupid whore!' He continued while nodding his head, 'You are not only stupid, as if that isn't enough on its own, but you are also a cheap, twisted whore. I am really sorry for myself for having wasted five years of my life with a sex maniac who has just decided to write a porn novel, in fact her true life story, which is a hardcore porn story to begin with. You don't deserve to be with me, I'm too good for you. You deserve to be with the likes of that Italian Film Director.'

Well, I should have seen it coming; I don't know what I was thinking when I gave him a copy of the chapter I had written on The Italian Film Director. Maybe even after five years I was still testing his love and whether he could fully accept me for what I am. The funny thing is, he hadn't been so keen on reading it in the first place. I had left it in his study room in Geneva before taking a flight back to London. I wanted his opinion on something that meant so much to me and that I had been working on so eagerly, typing away day and night, baring my soul in it. But now that I had finally got his opinion of the text and of me, I wasn't so sure; maybe it would have been better if I had kept it to myself. After all, he was the only man that I ever truly loved, he was the love of my life and I was losing him just because of some stupid book I was working on. I definitely wasn't playing the game according to the rules. Remember? Always make them think of you as some kind of a virgin. I was doing the complete opposite. By choice I had reminded him of my darker side, the side he had preferred to forget and kept hidden somewhere in the back of his mind. I just had to stretch out my hand and reach to the far corners of his brain and place it back on the very top section of the list. On top of naïve, good-hearted, trustworthy and modest. Now there was the word WHORE up there on the very top of the list, popping out whenever he thought of me.

But he knew of my relationship with the Italian Film Director from the very beginning, and it was an affair that had taken place way before I had started seeing him, so what was the big deal? For me it wasn't a phase that I was necessarily proud of but it had happened and I could not erase the past. At the end of the day I hadn't killed anyone or robbed a bank; I had just had an affair with a sleazy film director. What was more important: my love and loyalty to him in the present, or what I had been up to in the past? And of all people, who was he to judge me anyway, hadn't he told me on numerous occasions that he had slept with half of the female population in Istanbul and Geneva until he had met me? If it was a case of promiscuity, he definitely had more to be ashamed of. I had never judged him for his past, why couldn't he do the same for me?

He said he simply couldn't because we were not on equal terms here, he was a man and I was a woman. It was over between us. My eyes were full of tears and as I looked straight into his eyes all I could see was hate and disgust. I knew that he was being a complete asshole, but for some reason it didn't stop me from feeling pain. It's hard to think rationally when you've been long enough with someone to consider them as a part of your own reality. When, despite the fact that you have a relationship that is nowhere near close to being healthy and functional, you still find it difficult to turn the page. I guess I was still a little girl who was too scared to let go. A life without him felt as terrifying as being left naked among a group of Japanese tourists in Piccadilly Circus.

It was late 2004. A lot of things had changed in my life by then. I had finished my master's degree five years earlier and had been working for the past four and a half years at a high-end Public Relations Agency based in Mayfair. I had new friends. People from different fields of work: musicians, bankers, property developers, art dealers, yet they all had something in common: they were all ambitious people with a positive attitude towards life. They weren't lost souls looking for some route to destructive escapism. My friends had changed because I had changed. I had also been in a steady relationship for the past five years. Well, until that night, that is.

I met the Love of My Life a year before he became my

boyfriend. Although I was living in London and he was based in Geneva, we met at a dinner party in New York. He was an extremely good-looking Turkish man, one of the most handsome men I have ever laid eyes on. A guy in his mid-fifties, tall and fit with thick layers of light to dark blond hair (no he wasn't dying his hair), large distinctive blue eyes and a perfectly defined nose. In fact he was the epitome of beauty, charm and charisma. Although all of his suits were tailor-made by the finest of tailors and he wore shoes that were no less than five hundred pounds a pair, his look was never flashy but instead very refined and classy. He was the kind of man everybody could not help but stare at with curiosity and admiration whenever he walked into a room. He had the charm and grace you would associate with royalty. Yet in addition to his good looks and sophisticated image he was still a little boy at heart. He loved to drink and occasionally have a spliff and would laugh uncontrollably in his very own unique way, as if he was having some sort of a fit or something, whenever he found anything amusing regardless of the company he was in. And he knew anybody who was somebody: politicians, aristocrats, rich businessman, socialites and the whole shebang.

Still for some reason, although he had made it obvious that he was keen on me, on our first brief encounter, I was not so taken by him. I had enjoyed his company and was impressed by his good looks, but I was too unfocused in life to realise that the man who was seated right beside me at a dinner party was everything I could ever wish for in a man. That one day, I was going to fall madly and deeply in love with him. No, at that stage he was just another guy: good-looking, well mannered, highly entertaining and refined, yet still just another guy. Luckily, by the end of that night he had managed to exchange numbers with me.

Then he started calling me on a regular basis. Sometimes just to have a chat or at other times to let me know that he was coming to London soon. It was when I was hanging out with the night people. I was not interested in having a relationship with him or anyone else and when he did come to London to see me, I would either say I was busy, or travelling or simply too depressed to leave the house, or I would accept his dinner invitation but never go any further with him. He had even showed up with a Chanel watch in his hand at my doorstep one day when I had casually mentioned over the phone that my birthday was coming up soon. Finally becoming aware of my lack of interest in him, he stopped calling me and I really didn't care.

Nevertheless our paths were to cross again by pure coincidence after roughly a year had gone by, at another elite social gathering. It was sometime in mid-September. I was invited to a dinner party at a rich Jewish-Turkish businessman's house in Holland Park. As the butler of the house led me through the wide corridors of the huge mansion and into the large living room that was ornamented with antique furniture and expensive works of art, a Picasso there and a Chagall here, I saw the man who was to become the love of my life standing at the far end corner of the room with a drink in his hand talking to some girl I didn't recognize. After saying 'Hi' to a few people I made my way across the room and went over to join him. We started chatting away instantly as if we were two old friends who were able to break the ice in a matter of seconds. And we continued our deep conversation throughout dinner while he was seated opposite me. I can't remember what we talked about but what I do remember is the warm feeling of familiarity and the effortless free flow of our conversation. Although I declined his offer to spend the night with him that evening, after returning home I did realise that I strongly wanted him to be a part of my life. I was finally ready to let someone in and give myself up unconditionally, and was prepared to face the consequences; or at least so I thought.

How does one gain admission to a person's life in this lonely, self-absorbed, self-sufficient age that we live in? Yes, London is infested with singletons that stalk the city night and day, looking for their ideal mates yet who instead get easily distracted with superficial short-term flings. We're all able to convince ourselves that deep down all we want is to love and be loved but when it comes down to actually doing something about it, we're reluctant to break down the great wall of cynicism that we're encircled with. Let's face it, when it comes to relationships, we're nothing but a bunch of lazy, discontented idealists. Even if we ever do get to find that one special person who is able to meet our high set of criteria, soon enough we find ourselves too overwhelmed by the compromises that we need to make on a day-to-day basis for a relationship to work. We take things for granted. The time and energy-saving practicalities of modern-day living have somehow persuaded us to believe that the same rules can loosely apply to our personal lives as well. We guard our freedom of choice with harsh determination, yet somewhere in the back of our minds, we feel, we almost know for certain that we'd have a higher chance of fulfilment in our lives if we'd never tasted the endless possibilities that we have been fixed with, without choice.

As for me, I was in a *been there, done that* kind of frame of mind when I came across him for the second time. I had seen enough absurdity out there to write a novel. Yet, as usual, I had chosen the most unlikely candidate to start off a conventional relationship with: a twice-divorced, ageing playboy.

The following day when he called me from the airport as he was off to some other metropolitan city, I made my intentions clear to him by saying, 'I really like you and last night I became aware that we have this natural bond. I want to see you again and spend more time with you. When are you back in London?' He was back in a week's time and after that we simply hit it off.

For the first time in my life I was not only deeply in love but looked up to and respected a man. I knew I wasn't perfect but I was ready to change. And I did change. Not only because he wanted me to but also because I knew that the time had come. I changed my friends, I changed the way I dressed, I even changed my manicure. I stopped associating myself with vulgar people, people on the edge, people who had no ethics in life. I stopped wearing mini-skirts, stilettos and any kind of clothing that revealed too much flesh or made me look too sexed-up. Out went the Versace evening dresses and Gucci stilettos and in came the Armani and Max Mara suits. I replaced my La Perla lingerie, that I had in practically every colour of the rainbow, with Calvin Klein and Prada underwear in soft pastel hues, plain white, beige and black. I had my acrylic nails removed and went all natural. I became a member of a health club and started to work out on a weekly basis with a personal trainer. Yet, my transformation didn't happen over night. Every time he came over to London to see me or I joined him in Geneva, or we met up in some exotic destination, he would ask me subtly to change something about myself, and if, for some reason, I didn't take any notice of his advice, he would repeat it in a more firm manner, the next time we were to meet.

'Why do you have this desire to look like some kind of a high class prostitute…'

'Excuse me?' I responded with my eyes wide open.

'I told you before that I don't like you wearing skirts that reveal your ass to the rest of the world but I guess I didn't make myself clear enough.'

'No way am I revealing my ass to the rest of the world. You make it sound as if I'm wearing a micro-skirt; this is a decent length skirt. You are just being overly conservative. Just look around you: more than half of the women in this restaurant are wearing the same length skirt as me…'

At this point he leaned back in his seat and said, 'But you see, you're not just anybody; you are my girlfriend and my girlfriend should always dress like a refined, sophisticated lady.'

'What does that have to do with it? I can't believe that despite the fact that you've been living in Geneva for the past twenty-five years you still have such hang-ups.'

'Well,' he proudly said, 'you have to accept my terms if you want to be with me. I am a reasonable guy when it comes to many things; I just don't want my girlfriend to look like a hooker!'

After we had returned to our hotel room that evening he grabbed my skirt, as soon as I took it off, and cut it into two halves with a pair of scissors. He couldn't have made himself any clearer to me.

Whenever I would place my hand on my forehead to check on a pimple that was ready to surface he would reach out and slap my hand at that instant and say, 'Don't play with your skin! The more you play with it the worse it will get.'

'But...'

'No buts. Just do as I say!'

Whether it was a wine-tasting course at Christie's, French tuition lessons or driving lessons; he would always come up with new strategies for self-development. He would return with a bag-load of vitamins and medicine that he had got for me from a trip to Miami. During our daily phone conversations he would check up on me to see what I had for breakfast, lunch and dinner.

'Have a cereal for breakfast and freshly squeezed fruit juice. Pasta or any carbohydrate for lunch. Grilled fish or grilled chicken with assorted steamed vegetables or a salad for dinner. You can also have red meat once a week. And by the way, are you still taking those vitamins I got for you?'

I would call him while lying in the back seat of a cab after having left early from work with a trembling voice and say, 'I feel really ill. I think I'm going to die. I wish you were here.'

'What's wrong with you my love?'

I would reply with tears running down my cheeks, 'I feel all shivery and I have a sore throat.'

'Take three thousand milligrams of vitamin C, as soon as

you get home. Get yourself some soup from a supermarket on your way and then take two capsules of the Tylenol that I got for you. I'll call you back to check on you in half an hour.'

From day one, our relationship was founded on the grounds of a mentor-apprentice, father-daughter liaison. Whenever I was faced with any uncertainty in my day-to-day life (whether it involved what to wear to a dinner party, how to resolve various problems at work, or what present to buy for a girlfriend at her birthday) I would call him up and ask him for his advice, and after going through all the details with me so as to get the picture right, he would tell me what route to take. I felt like a big burden had finally lifted from my shoulders, as till then my indecisive nature had been a bit too overwhelming for me. No longer did I have to worry about what food to order at restaurants or what clothes to take for a weekend's trip to Tegernsee.

For the first time in my life I was with someone who believed in me and actually considered me as someone with great potential, someone who was very capable of developing herself, someone who already had endless personal qualities. He would say, while we were on site, appreciating the ecstatic architectural beauties of an ancient madrasa in Samarkand, 'This is amazing, ha? Now who would've thought that such breath-taking beauty would exist in a place like Uzbekistan? I was stunned when I first came here. That's why I asked you to come along with me on this business trip. I thought of you when I was here on my last trip. I said to myself, "My little bunny has to see this." I want you to have a worldly knowledge of places and different cultures and to develop yourself in every possible way.'

I would smile shyly, snuggle up to him and give him a warm

kiss on one cheek. Then he would continue, 'I see great potential in you. You know, you would also be a great wife and Mother because you're an affectionate, loving person with a strong sense of responsibility. And although you've had a lot of madness in your life, deep down inside, you are a person who has extremely strong ethics and family values. In fact you are one of the nicest people I have ever come across in my life. You have the heart of an angel. Whatever ludicrous nonsense you've gone through in life is all related back to your Father; he has really screwed you up big time.'

Even my relationship with my Father started to improve. Whenever I went to visit him in Istanbul I ceased to see him as the man who had caused so much emotional turmoil in my life and still had the capability to repeat his actions, but started to consider him as a man who had had his reasons for never being a good Father to me. Rather than judging him continuously for his past misconducts, I was finally ready to accept him for what he was and not allow him to get to me the way he had. And even if he ever did, I always knew I had the emotional support of my man to fall back on.

He really was able to bring out the best in me. I believe I was able to do the same with him. A year into our relationship he had also ceased to be the man who was highly impressed by the labels of things. He started to distance himself from his so-called best friends, who were mainly rich Turkish businessmen who only cared about having a good time but were never really there for one another when the going got tough. He became a deeper, more considerate and soft-natured man.

For the first time in my life I allowed a man to take me out on a shopping spree. It just seemed so natural for him to spoil me with designer clothes, precious jewellery and expensive watches. It no longer felt like a guy was buying me off; I was already his, body and soul. He was an extraordinarily generous man and his generosity did not derive from any hidden agenda; he just got immense pleasure from looking after and pleasing the ones he cared for, whether it was his girlfriend or his friends or anyone he knew who was in some sort of a financial struggle. He wasn't a multi-millionaire but he was well-off and didn't mind sharing his bank account with the ones close to him. Actually, with his strong international contacts he could have easily become one of the richest Turkish businessmen in the world, yet he was never calculating enough to be so. He simply couldn't find it in himself to make use of his contacts in that way. He said it made him feel cheap. Instead of taking, he preferred to give.

'That's my worst trait ever,' he would remark and then continue, 'there is no point in having a noble soul. The nicer you are to people, the more they take advantage of you. There is no room for decency in this world where personal interests and deceitfulness rules. But even though I am able to acknowledge this fact it's too late for me to put it into practice. Unfortunately, I can see that you're exactly the same as me. You have to learn how to use people before it's too late. You always have to ask yourself, how can so and so be a useful contact?'

I would grimace and reply, 'I can never be like that; I don't have it in me.'

'Then you have to force yourself, otherwise people will just use you.'

'I disagree with you. Not all relationships are based on some devious hidden agenda. I firmly believe that there are people out there who would give without expecting anything in return; who would be your best friend, a shoulder to cry on regardless of who you are. And after much soul searching I've come to the realisation that those are the kinds of people that I want to associate myself with. If you have a noble soul you're stuck with it from day one. It's pointless wasting time, trying to convert yourself into an inferior soul. Even if you are able to momentarily achieve it you'll only end up making yourself feel like a cheap prostitute.'

I remember how he had devotedly supported an old high school friend whom he hadn't seen for at least twenty years, as soon as he found out that he was penniless, fighting for his life after being diagnosed with lung cancer. All his so-called close and rich friends had looked the other way, whereas the Love of My Life had not only paid for all his medical expenses but was there by his bedside when he sadly passed away.

Yet the insecurities that were embedded in both of us were soon to resurface and disrupt the strong bond that had grown between us, and the mutual deep love and respect we shared for one another.

I was terrified of being rejected and abandoned. Whereas he was horrified just by the pure thought of being betrayed by a woman. I remember nearly drowning in Lake Geneva one summer evening, when we were out on a small boat with a friend of his. After an hour into watching the beautiful fireworks on display I told him that I was desperate to pee, and believe me I was. As the small boat had no toilet apart from an empty bucket I told him that we had to go back to the shore. He told me that I had to wait. How could I possibly wait, I was about to burst in my pants! No, I had to wait. The more I insisted, the more he seemed reluctant to go anywhere. At one point he lost his temper and yelled at me saying, 'Enough! We're here to enjoy the fireworks; I don't want to hear any more of your stupid nagging, okay?'

He simply treated me, in front of his friend, in a rather contemptuous manner as if I was some spoilt little girl who wouldn't take no for an answer, who was incapable of controlling her bodily urges. By ignoring my pleadings, at that instant, he had just proved to me that he really didn't care for me; for him I was nothing but some form of light-hearted entertainment. Suddenly this immense feeling of despair and frustration hit me like lightning and took over any sense of logic I had in me. I told him that I was going to jump and he said, 'Fine! Jump, pee and come back.'

And I jumped with the intention of not returning. I could see the lights of the city, I was going to swim to the shore, and I did. Well, sort of did. I remember that I was struggling, still dressed wearing a jumper, jeans and sneakers, swimming with all my strength, yet it seemed as if I was making very slow progress. Eventually when I was pretty close to the shore, my feet were still unable to touch the ground and at that very moment I felt that I had finally run out of fuel. It wasn't like I was trying to kill myself. I was just furious and wanted to get away from him, and I had, but it had just dawned on me that I might have to pay for my mad reaction with my life. 'So, is this how it's going to end?' I thought while still struggling with myself not to surrender to the cold, dark waters of the lake. Thousands of people die on this planet every day and if I die, I'll just end up being one of them. No longer an individual but just a name on a file with my date of birth and date of death registered. And they'll put down my cause of death as drowning. I thought of how saddened my Mother was going to be once she found out that her daughter had drowned because of mere stupidity in Lake Geneva. How could I do something like that to her? I don't think she would ever be able to fully recover after my death. I could never forgive myself for that. Though I needn't worry too much about it, as I would no longer exist anyway. Or maybe I would, but just at another frequency. Then at least I could haunt her, convince her that my spirit had found some sort of salvation. Maybe I could somehow persuade her that death hadn't turned out be such a bad option after all. No money issues, weight problems or terminal illnesses to deal with. I could hang out with her for a few weeks and keep her company. But what if that drove her into insanity and she ended up in a mental institute, right after she started telling everyone that she was hanging out with her dead daughter? God, death is such a huge responsibility and I don't really want to die anyway. What about the Love of My Life, would he have cared, felt any guilt at all? After all, it was his initial reaction that had triggered such anger and had set me off into a state of hysterics. I was just about out of breath and the lake water was at the tip of my tongue, waiting to stream in when I waved my right hand and cried for help. It was embarrassing but I had to do it. I just wasn't ready to die yet.

I saw someone jump into the water and soon the young man that was wearing a denim jacket, who was presumably Turkish, as he looked very Turkish, held onto me from the waist and brought me to the shore. I thanked him in English as I was really not interested in engaging in any small talk and asking him which part of Turkey he was from and so on. As the crowd watching the fireworks parted in order to allow me to go through, I felt like the mermaid Daryl Hannah in the eighties movie *Splash*. I had practically appeared out of nowhere yet in a less impressive manner. Then the security guards from a nearby hotel turned up by my side with their walkie-talkies and a large table cloth that they instantly wrapped around me. Suddenly I was surrounded left, right and centre by a crowd of people. I no longer felt like some mysterious mermaid woman, but more like a mad woman who had pulled some freakish stunt just to get people's attention. Like the ones who throw themselves bare naked into a football pitch right in the middle of a major league game. They were asking me all sorts of questions: had someone tried to drown me? Did I need to report anything to the police? Was I injured in any way? I told them that I was fine; nobody had tried to kill me and then asked them politely if I could possibly use their restroom. Soon after that they arranged a driver to drop me home.

While a young blond Swiss driver was driving me in a black Mercedes Benz back to the Love of My Life's house by the lake, and I was seated next to him still wrapped inside a white table cloth, he turned round to me and asked, 'So what really happened out there? Why did you have to swim to the shore like that?'

I looked at him and sighed for a moment hoping to come up with something more plausible to say to him. Then I just thought to myself, 'Why should I need to lie to a complete stranger?' I said, 'Well, I was desperate to pee and my boyfriend was reluctant to take me back to the shore so I jumped instead.'

The young man just looked at me with a blank expression on his face. I continued while nodding my head frantically, 'I really was desperate, I was in pain.'

No, this stranger was determined not to show any signs of sympathy or compassion for me, which made me feel worse than I already felt. As we continued to drive in complete silence, in my head I was still defending myself to him. 'What was I to do, ha, pee all over myself? You stupid cold-hearted Swiss!'

Then it suddenly hit me. By jumping into the lake and disappearing like that, I really had gone too far hadn't I? As I hadn't returned back to the boat there was even a chance that he thought that I had drowned or something. Or maybe he was still watching the fireworks with his friend. If he had really cared for me, wouldn't he have jumped after me? I wished I had the power to fake my own death. Then I would really know for sure if he ever loved me.

When the Love of My Life returned home, he was raging. He had already warned me about his temper. I remembered him saying, 'I know that you see me as an affectionate softy but if you ever push the wrong button with me, I could be so ruthless and unforgiving you could not even contemplate it. So don't ever take me for granted 'cause if you do, you'll be sorry. Believe me you will.'

He said, as soon as he came up to his doorstep and saw me standing there still wrapped in a tablecloth, 'It's over between us. I want you to pack your bags and leave in the morning. I cannot share my life with a lunatic. Now leave me alone; I am going to sleep,' and rushed off to his bedroom.

I lay awake all night crying by his side, begging for his forgiveness. Sometimes he would wake up from his deep sleep and tell me to either shut up or fuck off. Finally, sometime around 7 am I came to the harsh realization that it was over between us. It was pointless to disgrace myself any longer. I arranged my ticket back to London and after packing my suitcases I went back into his bedroom. He was awake. He lifted his head off the pillow and said, 'What do you want?'

I replied, without making eye contact, 'I'm leaving. I have a flight to catch. Thank you for everything.'

He asked, while he got up from his bed and made his way to the bathroom, 'What time is your flight?'

'6 pm.'

He said, patronizingly, as he returned from the bathroom wearing a bathrobe and sunglasses, 'How do you intend to spend all that time at the airport, you stupid idiot?'

I replied, still without making any eye contact, 'I don't know. The early flights were completely full and you asked me to leave in the morning so I'm leaving.'

He ordered me to sit down. I placed myself on one of the armchairs by his bed as he went to the kitchen to prepare himself a glass of whisky at 9 o'clock in the morning. 'What is the point of all this?' I thought. Then he came over with his glass of whisky, sat on the other armchair that was facing me and lit up a cigarillo. At first he started to giggle silently and the more he got into it the louder his laughter became. At one point I wasn't even certain, this time round, whether he was really having some sort of a fit or merely laughing. I said, with a worried look on my face, 'Hey, are you all right?'

He stopped for a second, lifted up his sunglasses to wipe off the tears from his eyes and then said, 'Remind me again what you did last night.'

'You know exactly what I did!'

'No, I want you to repeat to me what you did.'

'I jumped off the boat and swam to the shore.'

'...And please, I beg you to remind me the reason for your rational behaviour.'

'I jumped off the boat because I needed to pee. Satisfied? Can I please go now?'

He didn't reply to my question but continued to laugh out loud for another minute or two while I sat there looking confused. Apparently it was his way of saying, 'I forgive you.'

Whereas with him it was a different story. For him women were deceitful, lying little whores that could never be trusted. I found it astonishing that such words could come from a man who had been a total womaniser throughout his life. But I guess the reason that he had slept around with anything remotely good-looking that came his way was because he somehow felt this uncontrollable urge to get back at the female population. He was taking his revenge. Cheating before anyone had attempted to cheat on him; having the upper hand, so to speak. One day, while he was digging into a plate of risotto with garden vegetables at Toto's in Walton Street in Chelsea, he admitted that he had never shown any sign of pity, affection or love to any woman in his life. Then he added, 'You, for some reason, have changed all that. Maybe it's all down to old age.'

'So, if I had met you when you were in your twenties or thirties you would've treated me differently?'

'You can be sure of that! I would've just wanted to shag you. And the moment I did, I would've moved on to my next target and never looked back. You see, at that stage in my life I had women throwing themselves at me all the time. Sometimes it even got a bit too draining. Everybody use to call me "The Don". I was so spoilt and full of myself. If I had met you then, I wouldn't have been able to see right through you.'

When I asked about his two previous marriages he said, 'I was a terrible husband. I had no sense of responsibility towards my ex-wives. I was never at home. I would either be getting drunk in some nightclub with my male friends, or be in bed with other women. I hated being married. If it wasn't for my parents' persistence I would've never tied the knot with either of my wives. I kind of feel guilty now for the amount of nonsense they had to put up with because of me. I kind of screwed up their lives really.'

'Didn't you love them at all?'

'Who? My wives? You must be joking!'

He was a passionate lover, yet so was I, and although he would be highly aroused by how my intense desire for him translated into such playful actions of lust, just the thought that I was capable of performing such tasks would later set him off into a state of frustration and distrust. Sometimes when I expressed my horniness openly by first giving him a lusty look and then charging into him like some kind of wild animal, he would push me away and tell me to stop behaving like a complete slut. I was confused, but after a while I chose to control my sexual urges; I had no intention of pushing him away from me for any reason.

Before he had come into my life I had always been like some kind of vicious predator with men; I would target my prey, take them to bed and conduct the whole act single-handedly, while they would either lie back and enjoy themselves or follow my orders and do as I pleased. I was surprised to find out that in fact I was highly aroused by playing a submissive role instead. To that day, no one had ever brought it out in me, they had naturally assumed that I enjoyed being in control, which I did to a certain degree, but nowhere near as much as I did losing it. Little did my enemies know that what I expected from them was not to surrender but to actually fight back. Even though I enjoyed the initial power I was able to exercise over men in bed, soon enough I would be put off by their reluctance to stand up to me. I would cease to see them as sex objects and start seeing them as some useless stupid little toy I no longer wished to play with. He had somehow managed to see right through me.

With him sex wasn't a straightforward physical activity, where you would try two or three positions until Mr Big Willy could no longer hold his juices. No, with him the bedroom was more like an adult's playground where you could switch off and live out your fantasies, or at least imagine that you did. He loved talking dirty in bed and would go into every single little detail of what he wanted to do to me while he grabbed me all over with his strong, manly hands. Quite frequently, he would urge me to explain to him how I had been fucked by other men prior to him while he would take hold of me from behind, start kissing and biting into my neck, fondling my breasts, squeezing my nipples and pulling my hair with one hand while he would give me a firm slap on the bum with the other.

At first I would be wary of his request as I knew how insecure it made him feel to face up to my past. Becoming aware of my reluctance to continue, he would give me a starting point.

'So where were you? Where did he touch you first?'

But I would still be hesitant to answer back. Then he would repeat his questions more insistently: 'Tell me, I want to know how he screwed you! Were you in his flat? Was he all over you?'

'Yes,' I would unwillingly reply, 'we were in his flat, in his bedroom.'

'And would he start kissing you, while fondling your wet pussy by lifting your skirt up and sliding his hand down your knickers? Then what would he do? Would he take out his hard prick and want you to touch it and play with it?'

'Yes, and then he would push me onto the bed. I would tell him to stop but he wouldn't listen and then he would spread my legs wide open, place his weight on top of me and stick his penis forcefully inside of me.'

He would then ask, 'Did you like what he was doing to you? Did you say anything to him while he was all over you, screwing you like an animal?'

'Yes, I would tell him to fuck me harder.'

At that point the Love of My Life would get up and place

his erect penis at the gate entrance of my wet vagina, while I would place both legs on his shoulders, in order to help out, and then he would force his manhood inside me and say, 'Would he start fucking you like this, really hard?'

'Yes, that's exactly how he would be fucking me,' I would reply.

'And you love to be fucked like this, don't you?'

'Yes, I do very much.'

Yes, our sex life was not all that straightforward and we did have to rely on our imaginations more than anything else to keep it going, but strange as it may sound, the truth of the matter is, I had never felt more turned on by a man ever in my life. He was literally fucking my brains out.

Yet outside the bedroom, whenever I confided in him about my past relationships he would not show the same curiosity and enthusiasm. I had mentioned the Italian Film Director, the Bangladeshi Landlord, the Proofreader and a number of insignificant others; no, he wasn't amused at all at what he had to hear. Knowing that we had a totally different approach to how a woman should conduct herself sexually, he would impose his harsh, opinionated vision on me at the most inappropriate moments. He would say while having a romantic dinner at Mark's Club in Mayfair, that my previous actions were unacceptable, for most of my life I had behaved like a complete whore, luckily I had met him and with his help had transformed myself into a lady.

For me it wasn't a case of how many lovers a woman should have, as I believe it's all very relative, but why she chooses to live the experience in the first place. Before I had become involved with him, I had gone off track somehow but I guess I needed to go through such a phase. And by 'going off track' I don't mean to suggest that I had done anything wrong by having a large number of lovers. What I mean to say is that I was at a point in my life where I needed to experience, for a period of time, various escapist routes, which sometimes involved men and sometimes involved other things. He simply couldn't get it. For him it was all about pussies and cocks; he was too prejudiced to see my actions from a wider angle.

Two years into our relationship, I knew that he was the one, the one I wanted to spend the rest of my life with. Yet our feelings weren't mutual. He had no interest in repeating the same mistake all over again by getting married for the third time. More importantly, it was the twenty-nine-year age gap that made him so determined not to commit. He would explain to me in a sarcastic manner that in ten years' time there was a high chance that he would no longer be able to satisfy me sexually and I would probably start looking for it elsewhere. That I would end up sleeping with the plumber, the neighbour's pubescent son, the pizza delivery guy and so on. He said he could never be the joke of the town. I would try to explain that I never had any intention of making him into one but it never seemed to work.

It's funny that although at the start of our relationship he was always implying some future commitment by talking about having children with me, or moving to London to live together, now all that he said was that we had to enjoy it while it lasted. That eventually I was going to meet someone of my own age and start a future with him. I didn't want to meet anybody else; I had already met the person I wanted to be with, why did I have to be still on the search for another partner? And I didn't give a shit about his sexual performance or any other form of difficulty I had to face up to. Having him by my side was more than I could ever wish for. I told him that if he was to ever become bedridden I would look after him, I would even wipe his ass. It made him laugh but, no, I didn't know what I was saying. I was too young to understand these things. Eventually I would see him as some sort of a nuisance.

He did love me but only wanted me on his own terms. As I had opened up to him in every possible way, baring my soul and every concealed trait of my personality, trying ever so hard to please him in any way, I was not well enough equipped to deal with his rejection. Slowly I started to lose it. I would call him in the middle of the night and tell him that it was over, if he wasn't going to commit then I had no intention of wasting my time with him. He would say, 'If you want me out of your life then I'll go.'

I would hang up on him by smashing the phone on the wall and start crying, and crying a bit more, and some more till it was time to go to work. I was in no position to set foot out of the house. Yet I would call him the next day with a trembling voice and say that he ought to forget what I had suggested the night before, but soon enough I would repeat the whole scenario. Sometimes I wondered how he could put up with it all or even love such a creature that had lost any sense of pride and self-dignity.

I started to become less and less social. Usually after work I would be at home wasting time, doing this and that, just waiting for him to finish his meeting or his dinner or whatever it was that he was up to and call me, and if for any reason he hadn't called by midnight and his phone was switched off, I would spend the rest of the night crying myself to sleep, assuming that by now he had had enough and that he was never going to call me again. I was deeply and utterly infatuated with him. He had become the very reason for my existence. My work, my family, my friends did not mean a thing; all I wanted was him. I wanted him to be mine; mine forever. As I had opened up to him in such an unguarded manner, now I was too weak to close up again, I just couldn't do it. It was too late.

I remember one hot summer weekend, just before I was to join him in New York, I spent the whole weekend listening to his favourite singer, Charles Aznavour, continuously crying while drinking vodka. Finally I took a pair of scissors from one of the drawers in my bedroom and started to cut myself. I cut various parts of my arms and legs; not too deep but just enough to feel the intensity of the pain and to see the blood come rushing through my skin. I have to admit that I took a certain pleasure in what I was doing. I was punishing myself for being such a weak creature; for letting someone get to me the way he had. On Monday morning when I woke up, in a room full of empty vodka bottles, ashtrays bursting with cigarette butts and saw my legs and arms covered all over in cuts I realised that I had to stop. I either had to stop seeing him or I had to accept his terms and learn to live with it. So I chose the second option.

In our dimly lit room on Plaza Athenee, in New York, whilst watching TV in bed, he softly traced his hands over my bare legs. I felt a hint of pain as he ran his hands on top of my wounds.

'Hey, what's this?' he demanded as his hands came into contact for the second time with my uneven skin.

I pushed his hands away and said, 'What is what?'

He leaned towards the side table to switch on the side lamp while I quickly ran off to the bathroom to grab a bathrobe. When I came out, he ordered me to take it off.

'Can't we just watch the film? I really want to find out who committed those murders.'

'You have two options: you can either undress yourself or I will do it for you. If I were you I'd go for the first option.'

I sighed for a moment and then said, 'Well I have to warn you first. You're definitely not going to like what you see...'

As the bathrobe fell to the ground I was face to face with the look of shock in his eyes.

'How did this happen?... Did you do it yourself?'

I nodded shamefully.

'How can you do something like that to yourself?'

I didn't know what to say.

'Why did you do it?'

I smiled nervously and then said, 'See it as an expression of my love for you.'

Then he got out of bed, came up to me, wrapped his arms tightly around me and said, 'I am screwing you up big time, aren't I? The last thing I want to do is harm you. No, this is not what we're about.' Then he distanced himself from me, I looked into his eyes, they were moist. He said, 'I'll do anything you want me to...'

'Well, apart from being with me for the rest of your life.' Then I started to cry as he held me in his arms. He said, while gently stroking my hair, 'You know, you will always be the only woman I will ever love, but I cannot start all over again with someone who is twenty-nine years my junior. And besides, I'm old enough to know my own capabilities. I simply cannot do relationships in the conventional sense. If I am making you feel that miserable, maybe you should leave me?'

'No!' I shouted back.

'You're my little girl and I will do anything to make you happy, but you have to come to terms with the fact that our relationship will never last. Like all good things it will come to an end.'

'So, how long will our relationship last then?'

'It's up to you. But it's better that you find someone you can have a future with soon, rather than waste your time with me.'

'I don't want anyone else.'

'Just think for a second. Could you imagine how it would be to be living under the same roof as me?'

I nodded back enthusiastically.

'I'm such a pain to live with...'

'I'll put up with it!'

'But why should you have to put up with a grumpy, moody old man when you deserve the best?'

'Because I want to.'

'After two months, you'll either try to poison me or you'll run away.'

'I wish I could be a small insect and live inside one of your nostrils...'

'Listen to me,' he said while holding my chin up, 'I will always be in your life as a friend no matter what happens. Put that into that little brain of yours and don't you dare ever do something as stupid as that ever again. You hear me?' I shrugged my shoulders and then nodded back.

'When you return to London I want you to find yourself a good shrink. I'll take care of the expenses.'

When I returned to London, I started going on dates with guys who had the right credentials: right looks, right house, right job and so on. I was never genuinely interested of course, my heart was already taken; there was no room for anyone else. Yet it made me feel better, made me feel stronger that I was surrounded by a variety of rich successful bachelors who I simply could not care less about. They were either too superficial, too boring or too short. No one could possibly take *his* place. The Jewish jeweller's son was too fucked up, the Turkish Ambassador's son was too self-centred and the German investment banker was too stingy. I was able to decipher every one of them and was able to point out their worst personal traits after a single date.

As I am never good at keeping secrets, I would usually tell him about my unsuccessful attempts to replace him. He would listen quietly without making a single remark. I wasn't trying to make him jealous but to simply prove that it was useless for me to search for anyone when everything I could possibly want was staring me in the face.

One rainy autumn afternoon I was sitting uncomfortably on a leather armchair in the consulting room of a psychotherapist in Harley Street. It was my second appointment with him. He was a short, blond, chubby Dutch guy in his late thirties. He came into the room holding the questionnaire he had asked me to fill in a week ago. As he placed himself in a relaxed manner on the chair facing me he said, 'I had a chance to go through your answers but before talking to you about them, I want you to tell me a bit about your childhood.'

I wonder what he would do if I suddenly got up from my armchair, knelt beside him, started to unzip his trousers and then gave him a blowjob? I wonder what his reaction would be? Thank God he's not good-looking...'cause if he was, it would be too difficult to get that thought out of my head. But come on, I would never have the balls to do it! Still, I am such a sick-head for even coming up with something like that. But what if he's also been masturbating for a week thinking about *me* and he's dying of embarrassment right now for being such a wanker? Maybe he's created this scenario in his head that he keeps repeating night after night before climaxing and falling asleep. For instance, like one day I finally open up to him and say something like, 'A man has never understood me like you have. I don't know what I would've ever done without you.'

And then I give him this look of worship, like as if he was God or Marlon Brando or something. Then he comes up and gives me a warm hug and I say innocently, right before I sink my lips into his, 'I think I am falling in love with you.'

At first he responds to my kiss by kissing me back softly. Yet in a matter of seconds, feelings of affection are replaced by animalistic passion. He's on top of me, ripping my clothes off, as I lie submissively on the floor. And before you know it he's screwing me right in the middle of his consulting room. Yes, very professional of him indeed. Naturally he doesn't expect me to pay for his hourly fee that day. What if he does? Then, I guess, I would never see him again for being such a stingy, selfish bastard! Boy do I hate stingy men…

'Last week you mentioned that your Father was a diplomat and that you moved countries quite a few times while growing up. Did you ever face any adjustment difficulties?'

I replied with a blank expression on my face, 'I don't know. Well, I suppose so. But what does that have to do with me cutting myself? Is that like the new trend among diplomats' kids?'

'In order for me to be of any help to you, you have to open up to me. I sense fear in you. Are you scared of being criticized?'

I shrugged my shoulders with a bored look on my face.

'From the questionnaire I gave you I can see that you still have unresolved issues with your Father.'

'Don't we all?'

'Did he criticize you a lot, your Father?'

Suddenly I could hear my own heartbeat. I started breathing heavily. My hands were all sweaty. I wanted to answer back, but didn't know how or where to begin. I finally said, 'Everybody has issues with their parents but this doesn't justify…'

'Why are you being so defensive? Tell me about your Father. How did he treat you when you were a little girl?'

I took a deep breath and then said, 'He actually adored me when I was little girl. I was always on his lap. When I woke up in the mornings I would go to my parents' bedroom and we'd snuggle up for half an hour or so. It wasn't until we returned from Vancouver that he changed.'

'How old where you then?'

'Around twelve.'

'Did something happen for him to change his behaviour?'

'No, not really. I guess I just lost my childish appeal. I was no longer this cute kid he could cuddle up or play with.'

'So how did his behaviour change? Did he yell at you frequently? Did he hit you?'

I started breathing heavily again. 'Yes, he yelled at me quite a lot. He also hit me occasionally but it wasn't an ongoing theme,' I responded, without making any eye contact.

'So would you agree that your Father abused you psychologically as opposed to physically?'

'Yes,' I replied as I looked away to wipe away the tear that was running down my cheek.

'You know, there's nothing wrong with crying. I don't want you to hold back your tears.' I nodded as the frequency of my teardrops increased. He passed me a tissue box.

'This is so clichéd,' I thought to myself as I grabbed a tissue.

'...So your Father regularly lost his temper with you. What was the reason?'

'Well,' I said while holding tightly onto the piece of tissue in my hand, 'he just couldn't stand me. He always made me feel unwanted. Like I was a burden to him. Like he'd have preferred that I didn't exist. Sometimes there would be a reason for him losing his temper like when I got low grades at school, but usually it would be for something I had no control over...like if anything went missing in the house it was always my fault and I could never defend myself.'

'Why not?'

'You don't understand, with him…it would only make him angrier. I was scared of what he might do to me.'

'Now give me an example, in detail, of such an incident that took place between the two of you.'

'I'm not sure if I can remember, and even if I can it's too painful. Well, I remember one particular incident…but I don't know if I can tell it.'

'Of course you can,' he responded reassuringly.

After a few seconds had gone by I looked up at him and said, 'We had just got back from Vancouver. We were living in Ankara. It was sometime in the afternoon. The school bus had dropped me home late that day because the driver had got confused with the route he had to take. We were meant to go over to a friend of my parents for afternoon tea. As I got off the school bus I saw my parents waiting for me outside our apartment. My Father was furious with me for being late although it wasn't my fault. He yelled at me continuously until we got into the car and then there was silence. As we were driving along, and he was in the front at the wheel, we stopped at red lights. To ease the tension my Mother asked me how my day had been so far. The day before we had gone shopping together and she had bought me a new pair of shoes to wear to school. I had worn them to school for the first time that day. I told her that my new shoes had given me blisters. Then all of a sudden, I felt this hard slap on my face. I was unable to register where it came from at first. I was so shocked and frightened that I peed all over my uniform. My Father started yelling at me again, accusing me of being late and ruining their afternoon. And as for the stupid shoes, I had made the choice of buying them and he was going to check up on me every day to make sure that I had them on. I still vividly remember him saying, "You are going wear them even if you return from school with bleeding feet every day." I saw the look of fear in my Mother's eyes. Her face had gone bright red. She whispered to him, "What are you doing? She hasn't done anything wrong." He replied still shouting, "Shut up you stupid woman! No wonder your daughter is an idiot!"

'You see I was no longer his daughter; from the age of twelve I was only hers. I knelt down and started sobbing silently. He never could stand my crying. It made circumstances worse.'

I stopped and took another tissue from the box. My throat was dry, my nose was blocked as tears came streaming from my eyes and onto my face, chin, neck and all the way down to my collar.

'How often did such incidents occur?'

'I don't know. Usually, every other day. I tried every possible way to prevent them from happening, but he always found a little mistake I had somehow overlooked. Even the smallest of all things, like if I smiled in a certain way or if I dropped my knife while we were having dinner, had the potential to set him off. There was always this tension in our house when he was around. I never felt relaxed. Actually the first time I ever felt at ease in a home environment was when I moved to London and started living with this old Polish Lady in Islington.'

'How did you feel about yourself when your Father treated you like that?'

I blew my nose with the tissue and then replied, 'I was kind of aware that I hadn't done anything wrong yet I still felt guilty. Deep down, I still blamed myself for it. I always thought that there must be something seriously wrong with me or else why would he hate me like that? I really loved my Father. I still do. I guess I'm an idiot after all.'

'So you felt rejected?'

I nodded.

'Yet this didn't stop you from loving him.'

'No. I was *in* love with him. Not like I wanted to get into his pants or anything...'

Then becoming aware of the absurdity of what I had just said I stopped for a moment, giggled shyly and then continued.

'What I mean to say is that I idolized him. I was in love with the *idea* of him as opposed to him, I suppose. The art lover, the intellectual, the highly charming charismatic diplomat; *that's* what I was in love with. He was an exceptionally handsome man with a very sharp sense of humour. He had this unique air about him. He was my role model. I wanted to be exactly like him when I grew up.'

He leaned back in his chair for a moment and then said, 'From what you've been telling me, all I can see is a very insecure, frightened man. A man who uses his defenceless daughter to pour out the anger he feels towards himself. He never hated you. All along it was himself he couldn't stand.'

'But I just can't seem to understand why he had such a profound effect on me. It's not like he sexually abused me or anything.'

'But he did abuse you. Sometimes mental abuse can be just as forceful as physical abuse. What about your Mother? Why didn't she do anything about all this?'

'She did. Well, at least she did her best. You see, we were

terrified of him. When he lost his temper he would get this certain look in his eyes. The look of an insane man. The look of a man who's capable of anything. Like the look Gary Oldman has in *Leon*, when he pops that pill into his mouth, just when he's preparing himself for the kill. Did you ever see *Leon*?'

'I am not sure that I have.'

'It's one of my favourite movies. No matter how many times I watch it I always cry at the very end when Leon dies and Mathilda plants the plant, the only thing that's left of him, in the back garden of her school. It's so sad.'

'Let's get back to your Mother.'

I leaned backwards, sighed for a moment and then replied, 'Well, if it wasn't for my Mother I don't know where I would be today. Especially when we returned from Vancouver to Ankara and I was being bullied at home and was a total outcast at school, she was my only source of strength. She was all that I could cling on to.'

I stopped for a second to clear my throat and then continued, 'My Mother gave me the most crucial thing a parent can give to a child. She gave me unconditional love. She always went out of her way to make me aware that no matter what I do or what I become, she always will be there for me. Whenever I indulged in any self-destructive behaviour, I would always get to a point where I knew I had to stop for the sake of my Mother. She became my conscience.'

'So, the nature of your relationship with your Father compared to that with your Mother is one of extreme opposites?'

I thought for a second and then replied, 'I had never thought of it in that light but yes, you're right.'

As I made my way home that afternoon, walking in the rain which gently drizzled over me, I was frustrated with myself. Why was my past still haunting me? I thought that I had put everything behind me. Instead, all that I had done was bury my unresolved issues somewhere in the back of my subconscious. And they were still waiting to resurface whenever I became emotionally weak.

Then I remembered a conversation I had had with my Father two years down the line, when I had gone to Istanbul for a break. It was the first time he had opened up to me about the relationship he had had with his parents. I remember it was a sunny afternoon. We were sitting in our living room, while sipping our teas and nibbling a variety of delicious Turkish pastries. Both my Father's parents had died long before I was born so I had never had the chance to get to know my Grandfather or my Grandmother. My Grandfather had been a renowned and respected surgeon who had inevitably had power over many people's lives. That is, apart from his own. My Father said, while he gazed into the distance to recollect thoughts he had kept securely locked up in the back of his mind, 'My Father had a heart of gold. He was a lovely man. I never heard him once raise his voice at anyone. He was a real gentleman.'

Then he uncrossed his legs, sat up straight and leaned towards me from his armchair. I felt my heart jump as I recognized the look of hate that suddenly became apparent in his bulging brown eyes. The afternoon sun was directly hitting his face, yet he didn't seem to mind or even notice it.

'Whereas with my Mother, it was as if she had a heart of steel. She was cold, uncompromising and cruel. You know, when I was sixteen years old, she slapped me so hard on the face one day for some stupid little mistake I had made by accident that I had to walk around with my head facing down for days and wait for the bruise to fade away. Can you imagine how degrading that was for me? I wasn't a kid any longer, I was a young man but that didn't stop her. She was a very strong, dominant woman, my Mother. She never let anyone stand in her way. Although I loved my Father, I hated the fact that he never stood up for himself or us when she was around. He was a wimp.'

I find it astonishing to see how far a parent can screw up one's life. Yet I find it even more fascinating how the same scenario can go on and on for generations like some genetic disorder. My Father had been emotionally scarred by his Mother and now history was repeating itself. Would I ever be able to break the cycle?

A week later I was back at the consulting room of my therapist on a grey, cloudy afternoon. While he was sitting in complete silence, going through his notes, I came to the realisation that I was starting to warm to him. And no longer was I contemplating in my mind what his reaction would be if I ever gave him a blowjob. The mere thought of it made me giggle out loud. He looked up and said, 'You seem quite happy today.'

'Well, it's not like I am depressed twenty-four seven…'

'Yes, I am aware of that. The problem isn't that you get depressed from time to time. Everyone gets the blues; it's a part of human nature. What I am concerned about is the severity of your depressions.'

He placed his notes on the side table next to him, leaned

towards me and said, 'You could go on for weeks or even months without having any feelings of despair or unhappiness. Until a certain incident occurs, that is. An incident that triggers the turmoil of emotions that you have been unable to let go since you were a little girl. Fear of rejection, self-pity, self-loathing. All these mixed emotions and rigid sets of beliefs about yourself come out into the open. All of a sudden you are no longer the highly social and confident girl you have persuaded people and to a certain degree, yourself, that you are. You have to reach out to that little girl…'

I sprung out of my seat and cried out, 'Will you just stop it! Don't you dare give me that little girl nonsense. And what do you know, anyway? Just because I filled out some stupid questionnaire and talked to you about my past, you think you can judge me like that? And stop pretending that you really care for me. You don't give a shit about me. All you're after is your hundred pounds hourly fee!'

He just looked at me without saying a word. I could tell that he was pissed off but he was trying really hard not to show it.

I said, 'Okay, I'm sorry for being rude and mentioning your fee like that but you know I have a point.'

'You have so much anger in you.'

'Why do you have to justify all my actions?'

'Because without that you will never be able to understand why you do the things you do. Like why you cut yourself for instance. Maybe you think it's all down to your boyfriend or the relationship that you have with him. But in reality, harming yourself has more to do with yourself than it has to do with your relationship.'

He hesitated for an instant and then continued, 'Today I want to talk about your boyfriend. After all he was the one who persuaded you to come and see me.'

After giving him a reasonably honest summary of our relationship, he said, 'If this person is not willing to have a future with you, why are you still with him?'

I sighed for a moment and then responded, 'Because I love him, and he's my soul mate and I can't imagine a life without him…'

'But to what extent is he in your life to begin with? You were explaining that you meet up with him once or twice a month and don't spend more than four days together each time.'

'Well, we speak at least twice a day over the phone.'

'Yet you don't experience the day-to-day realities of what a relationship is all about. As a matter of fact, you both have your own separate lives. He has his life in Geneva and you have yours in London. And on top of all this, he doesn't want to have a future with you. Don't you think that you deserve something better?'

I kept silent.

'You're a smart, intelligent, good-looking girl. You have a lot going for you. Why not find someone of your own age to settle down with and have a future together?'

'Your talking like my Grandmother… Listen, maybe he hasn't got the right credentials on paper. And the fact that he doesn't want to ever settle down with me is a bit of a bummer but the bottom line is, he makes me happy.'

'Because he's the father figure you've been looking for all along.'

I kept quiet for a few seconds and just stared at the tissue box that was placed on the coffee table in front of me. Then I looked up at him and said, 'Maybe he is and what is so wrong with that anyway? We all have our hidden agendas when it comes to choosing partners.'

'But what if this hidden agenda prevents you from ever having a fulfilling relationship? What if you waste ten or even fifteen years of your life with this man? Then one day you turn to look back and all you see is a life…'

'Stop it! You're depressing me! Do you think depressing your patient is the right route to her recovery?'

'You have to stop clinging onto him.'

'I am not clinging onto him for God's sake!… Okay, maybe I am a little bit, but I'm not a clingy person by nature.'

'Yes you are.'

'You're really starting to annoy me again...'

'You want a substitute father figure that you can cling onto. The same way you've clung onto your Mother all these years. You have to let go.'

'Why don't you understand? I just can't!' I cried out loud with tears running down my face.

Yet, as time passed by and I continued to attend my weekly sessions of therapy I started to build up my defences against the Love of My Life, learned to switch off whenever I had to part with him and accept the fact that we had no future together. He no longer was the centre of my universe. He was just the brightest star among all the other stars. Nor was he fucking my brains out in bed either. I just found it amazingly difficult to let go and give myself up unconditionally, as I used to. It wasn't that I stopped seeing him as a man, or instead saw him merely as a father figure or a friend. No, my love for him was stronger than ever but still I had removed one crucial aspect of it. I guess in order to stay sane I had to somehow block the immense passion I felt for him, the passion that had been eating me up inside and making me act like a complete fool. I no longer felt infatuated with him; I just felt comfortable.

Unwillingly yet gradually I transformed myself into some sort of an ice maiden in bed. I always had an excuse in order not to sleep with him. Sometimes I had eaten too much, or had too much gas and would joke about how embarrassing it would be for me if right in the middle of our lovemaking I was to blow out a loud stinking fart. At first, when it was every other month that we were having sex as opposed to twice a night in the beginning, he seemed to prefer the new me. After all, my high sex drive had always made him feel insecure. He preferred to have a less sexually active woman by his side. And when I did have sex with him it was never the same and it never felt the same. Even when he would start talking dirty to me in bed, I was unable to let go and join him in his fantasy world.

Three years into our relationship our sex life had ceased to exist. Although every second I spent with him was special, I dreaded going to bed with him. I loved the feeling of security his presence would give me when he lay there next to me fast asleep, but I felt extremely anxious about those moments of awkwardness when we would get undressed and get into bed together just to have a good night's sleep. It just wasn't normal.

So there we were, *five* years into our relationship, having dinner by the serene waters of the Bosphorus when after calling me a stupid whore he told me that it was over between us. When I pleaded with him to reconsider he said, 'We haven't had sex for almost two years now. Do you think that I am a fool who isn't aware that you no longer desire me in any way?'

I didn't know how to answer him; all I could say to him was that I still loved him very much, even more than he could imagine, but he wasn't interested in what I had to say. Somehow something that had initially been as straightforward as two people being in love and wanting to spend time with each other had turned into something way too complicated.

When he dropped me at my Father's apartment I just sat there in the living room, in complete darkness for hours on end wondering if I was ready to let him go. I have to admit that I did send him a number of cheesy text messages like, 'I can't imagine a life without you', 'I'll do anything you want, please don't leave me', 'You mean the world to me', knowing that he was never going to reply to any one of them as he still hadn't learned text messaging, and even if he had he still wasn't going to reply. I did find it astonishing though that the guy who I had once seen as my saviour, who had filled in the emptiness in me, had now transformed into an abusive, uncompromising, cold-hearted monster. And here I was taking shelter at my Father's flat.

I don't know if it was old age, the divorce, or retirement, but over the years that I had been away, there had been a gradual, visible shift in my Father's behaviour. He had turned into an introverted, soft-natured man who spent hours on end doing research and reading on art, philosophy and politics in his study room. He was still in his own selfish little world and would simply switch off and stare at one of the paintings on the wall if I spoke to him about this or that, but the fact of the matter was that he was finally able to let go of his abusive ways. I so much wished that he had done it a lot earlier, as I strongly believe that it would have made a big difference to my life. I guess after his retirement and divorce, he was faced with the fear of being left on his own and realised that he had to change his behavioural pattern towards his daughter before it was too late.

And to this day, whenever I go back to Istanbul and visit my Father and see this darling old man, hooked in front of the TV set, watching the evening news, or some old Western movie, dressed in his pyjamas and slippers, I go over to give him a warm hug and feel grateful yet saddened at the same time. I realise how much we've both changed since we've been apart. I guess, as one grows older, one also realises that nothing stays the same. People change, places change, the whole equilibrium of your existence changes.

For an instant I did think about cutting myself up again. Maybe I could scrape his name on to my leg? But I didn't. I looked at the Max Mara bag that was lying on the floor. He had obviously bought me a present before reading my chapter. After our disastrous dinner that night he had asked the driver to take out the bag from the boot of the black Mercedes and to hand it to me. I had told him that I could not possibly accept it after what we had gone through at dinner. He said that it was either going to the bin or to me. I guess it was all the same for him. I took it reluctantly just to avoid creating a scene in front of my Father's apartment. Now it was too painful to even look at, let alone to open up and see what he had bought for me. I could picture him going into the store, the admiring glances of the female shop assistants while he tastefully chose what he liked to see me in. It made me feel so sad to picture him like that. You see, he might have poured every drop of anger he had on me that night, but a night of injustice was not enough to wipe away the five years of love and emotional support he had given me.

Yet he was right in a way; not about me being a stupid whore but that it was over between us. Whether it was for this or that reason, the bottom line is that we were unable to function as a normal couple any longer.

Was I ready to move on? Yes and no. I was ready to fly back to London, go back to work, join my friends and just get on with my life. If the worst came to the worst I could leave my privileged life in Chelsea, ship all my designer clothes back to Istanbul and move to Tibet and become a monk. As for love, no, I was not ready to move on and considering the amount of time it took to get over my very first love, I had plenty of time to waste with more mind-provoking experiences (that nevertheless had a hidden agenda).

That night I was certain that in a few months time I could see myself having an illicit affair with the President of Colombia or an MI5 agent or joining the Communist party. When I returned to London I was still hoping somewhere in the back of my mind that he would call. He never did. Some nights when I had too much to drink I would think of calling him but even in my state of drunkenness I was still able to acknowledge that we had passed the point of no return.

Whenever I felt too overwhelmed by my own thoughts I would call a friend or some random guy and go for a drink at my local bar. It's funny how you can go to the same venue year after year, and be served by the same bartenders and waiters, shake their hands and say, 'Hi, how are you?' just out of politeness and totally ignore the fact that these people have a separate life besides their work. It's not like they were born with the sole aspiration of serving people; they're people like you and me who have passions, dreams and their own tale to tell, if you're willing to spare them the time. It was difficult not to notice the bartender at my local bar, who was this tall, very handsome, blond, thirty-five year old Russian. One evening as I was sipping my glass of whisky by the bar, waiting for my date to show up, who was already ten minutes late, feeling rather exposed sitting there on my own, I started chatting with him. He asked me how my day had been so far to which I replied, 'The weather was so nice that I took a stroll down to the Serpentine Gallery.'

He told me that he was an artist, a conceptual artist and had recently published a book on his work. He said, 'My work here at the bar gives me the freedom to focus on my art as I have the mornings and afternoons free and the money is not bad either.'

I told him that I would love to take a look at his book. He said he had an extra copy behind the bar and then took it out and gave it to me. That night after my boring date with a Jewish South African multi-millionaire property developer, I went home and as I was lying in my bed I started to read his book with the intention of not finishing it. Yet the more I read about and examined his art, the more I was drawn into it. The book was honest, it was from the heart, it was written in a simple language but was still able to make a strong argument in the realm of art. 'Well, who would have thought?' I said out loud to myself before placing the book on the floor, and switching off the lamp to go to sleep.

A few days later I bumped into him by mere coincidence while I was rushing home from work on Old Brompton Road. He was wearing a dark grey coat. He even looked more handsome minus the horrible vest he needed to wear to work every day. I told him that I had gone through his book and that I thought it was amazing. He replied, 'I am really happy you enjoyed it. Your opinion means a lot to me.' Then he looked straight into my eyes and hesitantly asked, 'Would you like to see an exhibition with me one day?'

I felt as if I was just sixteen, being asked out on a date by a guy I fancied at school. I said with a shy expression on my face, 'I'll think about it.'

He then said, 'I really like you. You must already have noticed that by now. I don't want to be pushy in any way so if I am you must tell me, but I would really like to see you.'

I told him that, yes, I could consider the possibility of going to see a show with him, if and when I had some free time available.

What can I say? I was in the mood to play hard to get. It's quite funny that whenever I play the game, which rarely happens, it's always with the wrong guy. Like I never play hard to get with the playboys I come across in Tramp, but instead I choose to do it with a guy who hasn't got a streak of arrogance or insincerity in him. He asked for my mobile number and I gave it to him with a sign of hesitance. The next day around three in the afternoon he called me. Instead of going to see a show we decided to meet at another local bar in Chelsea.

While we were sipping our glasses of cold white wine and he was talking to me about his work, his family and his art, I was wondering whether I could ever fall for someone like him. Whatever he was talking about, I was unable to detect a single trace of inferiority complex, low self-esteem, irrational thinking, big-headedness or self-centredness. And funnily enough when I spoke back at him I was able to trace some of those traits, if not all, in myself. I felt like a complete asshole next to this pure, decent and innocent being. He didn't have any issues; he was almost too straightforward for me. It suddenly made me become fully aware that I was the one with all the issues.

The next morning I woke up with the realization that I wasn't alone in bed. The Bartender pulled me towards him and wrapped his arms around me while giving me a warm, affectionate kiss on my neck. I just lay still, asking myself if he was what I really wanted. Suddenly I had flashbacks from the previous night. After finishing our drinks at the bar I had invited him back to my flat. I had been recently promoted at work and could finally afford a small one-bedroom flat in Roland Gardens in South Kensington. We had chatted away for hours while listening to some tacky Turkish music that he had insisted I play. I had told him how I despised living in a capitalist society which transformed people into consumer junkies and where everything had the potential of being turned into a commodity. He had told me that he agreed with me to a certain extent.

I had asked him how life had been in the former Soviet Union and if he ever missed it. He had replied, 'Communism degrades people. I remember the time when my parents had a serious argument over just a single cigarette that they had found hidden in the back of one of the drawers at our home.'

I had never seen things from that perspective and what did I know anyway? It was way too easy to make assumptions while looking down at the world from an ivory tower. I recalled how he had listened attentively when I mentioned the book I was working on. Then I remembered that, at one point, he had knelt down beside me and held my hand, looked into my eyes and had said, 'You are a very special lady.' He had placed his index finger on my forehead and had continued, 'But more importantly I like to know what goes on in here.' Then I recalled that around two in the morning when we were both drunk he had said, 'I want to make love to you' to which I had replied, 'You mean, you want to fuck me?' He had smiled shyly and said, 'I prefer to call it "making love".' 'All it is at the end of the day is fucking,' I had answered back. I had then told him that he could stay over but that I didn't feel like going any further with him. He had told me that he would love to just snuggle and fall asleep with me. Finally I remembered him whispering, 'I fell in love with you the moment I saw you enter the bar,' just before I fell asleep.

It was ten o'clock in the morning and I was still lying there in his arms after going through some of the highlights of the previous evening in my mind. I pulled away from him and got up. I said as I stood in front of him, 'I believe that I have to be clear on a few things here. I am not really sure of what I want from you and I don't want to lead you on or hurt you in any way. I have a lot of issues with men.'

'I can feel that you're emotionally immature.'

That wasn't quite what I wanted to hear but I knew that on some level he was right. I said, 'Well, yes, when it comes to men I can be emotionally immature and a commitment freak and for the most part I either see men as sex objects or get into relationships as if I am going on a roller-coaster ride; just purely for the thrill of it.'

'Don't you think it's time to change?'

'Well, I do, I guess. I am supposed to anyway; I cannot go on like this forever.' I sighed for a few seconds while trying to gather my thoughts and then I continued, 'I don't know if I will ever be able to change but I can still see a light at the end of the tunnel. It's weak but it's there.'

He smiled and said, 'I think you should include that line in your book.'

10

Fireworks

It's October 2005. I can hear the screams and laughter of children coming from the living room down the hall. The children aren't mine, nor is the house. I'm just staying here until I can get back on my feet again. You see, I got fired. It wasn't my fault really; our company went bankrupt. So I've been unemployed for the past eight months. I tried to get a new job straight after but no one would hire me. I was either not qualified enough or over-qualified. You know how good I am with handling rejection. People say that I really shouldn't take it personally but I do. They say that I have to be both patient and lucky. I know that they're right but this still doesn't prevent me from feeling like a complete loser. My flatmate has been on the phone for the past hour in the room next door. He was my boyfriend just a day ago; now he's my flatmate. The kids are his (he got divorced two years ago) and so is the four-bedroom flat he's renting at the Little Boltons in Chelsea. Funny how I always wanted to live on this street. I actually helped him find the flat. When I was drained out of my brains last spring, sending CVs, filling out work application forms and receiving rejection letters (*We were very impressed with your CV. Having said that, unfortunately we find you unsuitable for the position. We wish you all the very best of luck*), all at once he called me one day.

I told him with a trembling voice that I was fucked up big

time. He had never seen or heard me cry before. We had known each other for eight years so that was a big achievement for me.

'Come on! You'll manage. You're a strong girl!'

'Strong my ass,' I thought and then responded, 'Correction. I was strong. I have been here for over ten years. I did everything to stay here. I went against all the odds. And what was it all for? Is London really worth fighting for? What do I get in return?'

'You're just saying that because you're feeling a bit down...'

'Feeling a bit down?' I cried out. 'I don't even know if I'm able to pay the rent next month unless I sell my ass to a Middle Eastern Prince? Too bad he's dead!'

'Who's dead? What are you talking about?'

'Oh nothing. Just nonsense.'

'I didn't know that it was that bad...'

'Yep. That's how London is. But you know what the real problem is? If I leave London I have nowhere else to go. That's the scariest bit. Going back to Istanbul would just be like accepting my own defeat. As soon as I return people would start asking, "So did you get homesick in the end?" and I would shamefully admit to them saying, "No, I didn't actually; I just didn't have an option." How sad is that? And you know what? Whenever I go back to Turkey I observe things with the eye of an outsider. Turkey has become foreign territory for me. Moving back to Turkey would mean starting all over again. I really don't have the strength to start all over again. I used to be so good at it before.'

'You don't have to start all over again; you just have to be patient. Listen, I know that it's only a matter of months until you get your shit sorted out. I have to move out of my house in Pimlico in a month's time. I've been earning quite a lot recently. Enough to actually rent a bigger apartment in a nicer area so why don't you come and live with me? I can even lend you some money. I know I'm being very direct here but I really need a friend, a companion. At least we can help each other out.'

Apart from having a roof over my head I also needed a companion of some sort so I accepted his offer.

Two weeks before we were meant to move into our flat in the Little Boltons he called me from Heathrow Airport. He was on his way to Istanbul to meet up with this girl he had the hots for. Then, out of the blue he said, 'I don't know why I have to change countries to find love, when all I could ever wish for is by my side.'

I said, 'What?' and then let out a nervous giggle.

'Would you ever marry me, if I asked you to?'

He had seriously got me off guard. I replied, 'I am not the marrying type. But I could live with you and I am going to live with you anyway. What I am trying to say here is...' I took a deep breath and shouted to get my point across to him, 'we could be a couple, lovers, partners, whatever they call it.' I hesitated for a second and then said, 'Sorry I take it back; not lovers in the fuck buddies sense of the word. I want it to be serious.'

'A woman who knows what she wants,' I thought to myself. Shit was I changing, or what? But then again why nag about wanting to be serious with him when the guy is already talking about marriage and is moving in with you in two weeks' time. I sense a sign of insecurity, or better, a fear of REJECTION. Shush will you! This is a crucial moment in your life and you're fucking it all up by being self-critical in your head.

He replied, 'I want it to be serious too. Since my divorce, I've had my share of the game. I'm tired; I want to settle down. And I want it to be with you.'

When he returned two days later from Istanbul, that very same day I moved into his house in Pimlico. Was I in love with him? No, not really. But he was one of my best male friends and he turned out to be quite good in bed so what was the problem? After all, what more can a girl want? Love perhaps? I didn't want to waste my time looking for love in the same way that I was reluctant to spend a pound on a lottery ticket. Nor did I have any intention of throwing away another decade of my life, while trying to live out my twisted fantasies. I just came to the logical conclusion that as we were compatible mentally and physically, we had a solid foundation to work on.

Three weeks into our relationship we were in a taxi, driving from the Ciragan Kempinski Hotel after we had checked in and dropped off our luggage. We were in Istanbul for a romantic long weekend, just to unwind and maybe check out some of the open-air restaurants and nightclubs that had opened up for the summer season. We also wanted to buy a few new items for our unfurnished home. The driver said, 'Where do you want to go?' 'To the Grand Bazaar,[16] please,' he replied. It was

16 The Grand Bazaar, is one of the main tourist attractions in Istanbul. It's an ancient shopping mall that was built in 1464, on the orders of Mehmet II 'The Conqueror'. It's pretty huge with 4,400 shops, and 64 streets. When I was living in Istanbul I considered the Grand Bazaar as being outdated and tacky. But since I've moved to London I try to go there whenever I'm back in Istanbul. What I love about shopping in the Grand Bazaar is the bargaining; it can be such a challenge. Yet I have to admit that the persistent, saucy attitude of the merchants can sometimes get on one's nerves.

two o'clock in the afternoon. I put the window down to get some fresh air. It was burning hot. Half an hour's drive later we found ourselves at a carpet shop, looking at carpets, while taking short sips from our Turkish coffees. After staring for a second or two at a carpet the shop owner had brought to our attention, he said, 'I want you to decide. Take as much time as you like. But I just want you to know that it's your call.'

I just sat there with a frozen grin on my face while trying to figure out what was happening to me.

Okay, is it steaming hot in here or is it just me?... Shit, I can hear my own heartbeat! Maybe I'm just about to have a heart attack, although I'm pretty young to have one? Somebody please help me, I think I can't breathe... I wish I could disappear just now. Like *tadaa*: now you see me; now you don't... Oh my God! I know what this is, I am having a panic attack right in the middle of a carpet shop in the Grand Bazaar. Definitely, the worst place to have one. Not only is the shop overcrowded and cramped but even if I run out now I'll be going round in circles forever until I find the nearest exit. I'm stuck in a goddamn labyrinth... Okay just relax for a second, will you? Why are you doing this to yourself? Half of the female population would want to be in your shoes. You're not only with a guy who wants to commit, but he's nice enough to even let you choose the carpet. To hell with the carpet and to hell with the guy! I just want to be left alone! Oh God, I feel like I'm going to drown...

I nervously lit up a cigarette.

He said, 'What do you think of this one?'

I gave a glance at the carpet that was spread with all its glory in front of my eyes. I got up timidly and started examining it.

Don't take things so seriously for god's sake. See it like you're doing him a favour. Whether you're with him or not, he needs a large fucking carpet for his living room... Oh so, it's his living room now. What happened to our living room, our home? Just shut up and listen will you! All you're doing here is being generous enough to share your refined taste in carpets. That's all, so just snap out of it.

Finally after managing to block all the questions and doubts that were popping up in my head, for a brief moment I carefully examined the carpet and then said while I lifted my head up and looked at the shop owner, 'Yeah, I think this one would be great. The soft hues, the faded, worn-out antique look.'

Let me just point out to you that it's damn hard to act all cheerful and relaxed, while you're on a romantic weekend break with your boyfriend, when the mere reality of his existence makes you want to jump off the Bosphorus Bridge. Whether we were sitting at a candle-lit dinner at Sunset Bar and Grill, with a breathtaking view of the Bosphorus, or he was rubbing sun protection cream on my thighs by the hotel pool, in my mind I was going out of my way to persuade myself that this was just a phase.

And when you're in a relationship that you don't feel confident about, the most insignificant details are enough to justify your doubts. Any slight flaw in his personality or physical appearance has the potential to irritate you like nobody's business. Like suddenly noticing his hideous taste in shoes. 'The guy has no sense of style for God's sake. Look at the shoes he's wearing, the Love of My Life would've never worn a pair of shoes with a massive buckle engraved "Hugo Boss". How unrefined is that, like he wants to shout from the roof tops that he's bought a pair of lousy shoes from Hugo Boss?… I like tall men, I've always liked tall men. The bastard's been lying about his height. He said that he was two centimeters taller than me. Taller my ass. If I end up marrying him I will be forced to give away all my high-heeled shoes to charity. But what's more important; the shoes or the guy? I think the question answers itself.'

When we returned from Istanbul, I was in our flat on a Tuesday afternoon, sitting on the floor of our living room, playing with my mobile phone while he was still at work.

'Am I really getting into something that has no future or am I going through just a phase? My Mother reckons that it's just a phase but she's been telling me that for years; everything I go through is just a phase for her. I wish somebody could just tell me what to do instead of me having to lose my mind over it. What if I called the Love of My Life? He'd be able to tell me what to do. I wish I was with him instead anyway. I can never love anyone like I loved him. Maybe this is all happening because I still haven't got him out of my system.' Nervously I dialled his number.

He picked up after four rings.

'Hi, it's me.'

'Hi, how are you?' he responded with a cold, distant tone in his voice.

'I'm fine, I suppose. Well, I got fired a couple of months ago.'

'Sorry to hear that. Are you still in London?'

'Yes, still in good old London.' I closed my eyes as I said, 'I'm actually living with someone. Remember my Turkish banker friend who got divorced two years ago? The one who works for Deutsche Bank? Well, it's him.'

'Well, I wish you all the happiness,' he replied in a sarcastic manner.

'But that's the thing. I'm not happy. I mean, he's a good guy, we've recently moved to a spacious flat in the Little Boltons. Everything seems to be perfect apart from how I feel deep down inside.'

My voice began to tremble as I continued, 'You always used to tell me to find someone I could have a future with and I did. He's successful, single, seven years my senior and reasonably good-looking, although he's a bit short, but the thought of spending the rest of my life with him sends shivers down my spine. I still miss you. I told you that I could never replace you and now here's the proof!'

After a brief moment of silence he cleared his throat and then replied, 'Enough! How dare you call me like that, just out of the blue to tell me who your latest screw is!'

'He's not just some guy I am having sex with. I am trying to have a functional relationship here...'

'Fuck you!'

He slammed the phone on my face. Was he having a bad day or what? After all we had been through is that all he had left to say to me? FUCK YOU? What about being my friend no matter what happens?

'What on earth am I doing here, calling up Mr Commitment Freak to sort out my commitment issues?' I thought. At least in our brief phone conversation he had given me a glimpse of what I had been so desperately missing for the past months. Did I really want to return to how things were? The answer was simply no.

Suddenly everything seemed irrelevant apart from one thing: I was in a relationship that promised a future and I was going to do everything in my power to make it work. And as for his unrefined taste in shoes: a shopping spree in Jermyn Street would resolve the problem.

Naturally everything didn't go as smoothly as I thought it would. Making a relationship work is one of the most difficult tasks on this planet, especially when both parties are not willing to compromise up to the level where they give in to losing their own individuality. Like one does when one falls in love. We live in the true age of romanticism, when love no longer needs to conquer all; it just needs to conquer itself. To prove that on its own, it's able to survive. If not for eternity, at least for an odd year or two.

You would've thought that eight years is a long enough time to figure someone out. Well you'd be wrong. For the past eight years that I had known him he always came across as a laid-back, soft natured, open-minded, sexually liberal guy with a great sense of humour. Okay, I had also noticed that he was a bit insecure and unreliable at times but nobody is perfect right? Yet I was completely ignorant of one crucial aspect of human nature. That in fact knowing someone is not a question of whether or not you can ever come close to deciphering his or her true nature. You see, even if we make ourselves believe that we know somebody like a book; all that we really know is what that person consciously or subconsciously chooses to reveal to us. Who we are is not only circumstantial but also dependent on what the other person or persons that we interact with inspire us to be. What I knew of him for eight years was nothing but a combination of what he wanted me to know and what I had encouraged him to be. Now that our circumstances had changed, I was simply in the process of experiencing the outcome of what me plus him in a relationship living under the same roof would generate.

He would snuggle up to me after a wild session of sex and say, 'I would love to hug and fall asleep with you. Why don't we ever do that?'

'Because I can't; I'm claustrophobic. Like even if I tried to, as soon as you fell asleep I would have this uncontrollable desire to move every single part of my body.'

'That's strange. You see I'm a very tactile person whereas you are…'

'Not?'

I knew that I had to compromise so I allowed our legs to touch as we fell asleep.

He once came home early from work for us to go to Peter Jones and buy some home appliances. As he entered the living room and placed himself next to me on the sofa he gave me a long passionate kiss. Then he looked at me and said, 'I can't believe it; I have a hard on.'

Feeling confused about how I ought to react I uncomfortably replied, 'Okay, that's a good sign, that you have a hard on merely after just one kiss.' I looked at my watch straight after and said, 'Well then, it's five o'clock so I think we should make a move soon or else the store will close.'

'So no time for a blowjob I gather?'

I nodded and then said, 'Come on, lets make a move,' while trying ever so hard to disregard the apparent look of discontent in his dark brown eyes.

Actually I would be confronted with the same look whenever I wasn't up for anything that he was. A look that translated into something like, 'You don't love me, or desire me in anyway.' I remembered a particular thing he had mentioned, when we were still just friends, about this Brazilian woman he had dated for a year straight after his divorce.

'She's amazing. Like whenever I get a hard on she'll give me a blowjob.'

Whereas I preferred to go to Peter Jones instead... When walking around in the kitchen appliances department of Peter Jones, while I was confronted with the same look of discontent each time I gave him a glance, I kept questioning myself as to why I had behaved the way I had. Like was a blowjob too much to ask for? But then again it wasn't like I never gave him one. I just wasn't as sexually stimulated as he was at that particular moment in time. I could have pretended and done it as a favour but wasn't sex a sharing of mutual pleasures?

Whenever I was by his side I would take a break from holding his hand only to light a cigarette. I would continuously push myself to prove to him that he was the centre of my attention. Yet I still somehow felt that it wasn't enough for him. No matter what I did, I still wasn't able to fill this big void inside him that demanded constant reassurance.

Although his constant attention-seeking nature would frequently get on my nerves I would force myself to see things in a bigger picture.

'After all the shit that you've been through, do you think that you can still waste your time searching for perfection? You can find a guy who's more confident than him, who is taller than him and who has a better taste in shoes than him. Yet as soon as you do you'll be faced with a different set of imperfections. Don't take what you have for granted. This image that you have in your head, the image of the ideal man for you is just a fantasy; it's never attainable.'

Yet as weeks passed and I started to adjust to my new conventional life, I genuinely felt that I could see myself falling in love with him. I began to impatiently wait for his phone calls while he was at work and whenever he went for his short business trips to Istanbul I would count the days and wait for his return. With each day, to discover another of his routine habits, a certain behavioural trait that I had not been made aware of in the eight years that I knew him as a friend, was not only comforting but special.

Often enough I would catch him running to the loo with the latest edition of my *Vanity Fair* magazine.

'Hey, wait a minute, I haven't finished looking at it yet!' I would shout at him from across the corridor.

'You can have it back in ten minutes.'

'Is that how long it takes for you to take a dump?'

He would smile shyly and say, 'Stop it! You're embarrassing me…'

He would call me on his way from work and say, 'I'll be stopping over at Sainsbury's. What would you like me to get you?'

'I don't know, what do you feel like having for dinner? And please don't say hummus with pitta bread. Otherwise you're going to start growing chickpeas inside your tummy!'

'Hummus is meant to be an aphrodisiac...'

'How come you're the only person who's ever told me that? I think you're just trying to justify your addiction. And just for the record, you're the last person who needs an aphrodisiac!'

'You reckon?'

'Well, unless you want to start drilling walls.'

I remember calling him around ten in the morning one day. 'Hi, it's me.'

'Did you just get up?'

'Well, half an hour ago,' I responded and then said, 'What time do you think you'll be home tonight?'

'Probably around seven; why do you ask?'

'Because, well, I am going to cook for you.'

'Really?'

'Yes, and I haven't done it for ages so if it ends up tasting crap please don't be judgemental. I mean, I don't want you to lie but don't be harsh about it.'

'You don't have to cook for me.'

'I know that I don't have to, but I want to.'

I spent the rest of the day in the kitchen and I would call my Mother every hour to make sure that I was getting the recipes right.

By the time the clock hit seven I had set the dining table and placed a plate of Müjver[17], a plate of aubergine salad and a plate

17 Zucchini pancakes with scallion, Feta cheese, eggs, flour and fresh dill and parsley.

of leek with rice, onions and carrots cooked in olive oil in the centre of the table.

As soon as he arrived home, entered the living room and saw what I had prepared for him he said, 'Wow!'

'It's not much but I thought I'd start with the easier stuff.'

'Come on, Müjver is not meant to be that easy.'

After he had seated himself at the table and had tasted, and to my joy, almost finished with great appetite what I had prepared for him, he said, 'It's amazing. No, seriously, everything tastes delicious.'

'I am glad you enjoyed it,' I responded with a warm smile.

'But...'

'But what?'

'Don't take it the wrong way, but I don't like a woman cooking for me.'

'But, why?'

'I don't know. I guess, I am really not into the whole "domestic goddess" thing. It makes a woman unsexy.'

I looked down and said, 'I see.'

Three months down the line, I was having a relaxed dinner with him at an open-air restaurant by the Duke of York's barracks off the King's Road in Chelsea. By this time I had told everybody, including my Father, that I was in a serious relationship. To be frank with you, I was showing off a little.

Yes everybody, I am in a fucking relationship. No longer am I looking for adventure. Those days are over now. You never thought I had it in me right? Well, you were damn wrong! Eat your hearts out! I was feeling overly proud of myself, for having proved everyone wrong, and most importantly myself.

Right in the middle of our main courses, while we were making plans for our two-week summer break in his summer house in Bodrum in the Southern coast of Turkey, he excused himself from the table and said that he was desperate to pee. Ten minutes later, he returned from the restroom with a funny look on his face. His eyes were wide open. He looked shocked and traumatized.

I said, 'What is it?'

He just kept continuing to stare at my face with the same funny look.

'Is it serious?'

He nodded.

'Is it about us?'

He nodded again.

'Just spill it out for God's sake! Otherwise we'll be here until they close the restaurant.'

He sat back down nervously on his chair and then said, 'I love being with you. Spending time with you. Kidding around with you. We have great chemistry in bed. But the thing is, I don't feel any fireworks. It's as if we're just an old couple. I never had any fireworks with my wife and that's why I divorced her. Since then I've had fireworks but they've never lasted.'

'Could this all be because fireworks never last?'

'Probably, but I am a romantic. I know that we have our special moments but I don't want just "moments". I want an intense relationship and I want the intensity to last forever. I want us to kiss for hours in bed everyday when we wake up. Even when at work, I want to be on the phone with you the whole day.'

'We talk at least twice a day.'

'I know we do but that's not enough for me. What we have is not enough for me.'

'What you want is an idealised version of what a relationship ought to be. Even if you have the kind of intense relationship that you're talking about; soon enough you'll get to a point where you are unable to experience the same intensity every single day. Don't you ever stop for a moment to think what happens a year after Richard Gere sweeps Julia Roberts off her feet in *Pretty Woman*? Or if Humphrey Bogart and Ingrid Bergman never had to part like that in *Casablanca*? Do you really think that the intensity of what they had would last forever? People are complex beings. We have our mood swings...'

'Your mood swings get on my nerves. Like you're really cranky in the mornings.'

'It's not personal. Ask my Mother.'

'Even so I can't help it; I take it personally. And sometimes it's as if you're in your own world.'

'I agree. Sometimes, I am in a world of my own. All I really am is a fucked-up dreamer.'

'You're not fucked up. You're a unique woman. You are like a noble princess and a mad artist, condensed into one person. The person who's going to be with you should be fully aware of that. He should give you your space and respect that. I just don't think I'm going to be that person.'

'I can't believe you're doing this to me now!'

'I am sorry. But we're not in love, are we?' Then he looked straight into my eyes and asked, 'Do you love me?'

Did I love him? I asked myself right there and then. Difficult question to answer when being rejected like that. But come on; at least be honest to yourself. You care for him, you like screwing him and you're ready to dedicate the rest of your life to him but that's just about it, right? You might feel that it's about to happen any day now but the guy is getting a bit impatient here. Should you be honest? I've been honest all my life; I am tired of being truthful and honest. For once in my life I want to be tactical and see where it's going to get me.

I replied, 'I'm not answering that question.'

'Why not?'

'What's the point of answering such a question when you've already told me that you don't love me? What I feel from this point onwards has no relevance.'

'But just tell me anyway?'

'Fuck you!'

'Come on, I don't want you to hate me.'

'And I don't want to be dumped, but there are some things that you have no control over in life,' I said while shaking my legs neurotically under the table. I took out a cigarette from the cigarette packet that was lying on the table. I timidly lit it up and said, 'So, what's going to happen now?'

'I still want us to live together. Nothing will change. We'll just return to being friends again. I really love you, but I am not in love with you.'

'Perfect. Of all people, I didn't think that you'd screw me like this, you bastard.'

'Come on, don't be so harsh on me. You're my best friend. I just wanted to be honest with you. I've been thinking about this since we went on that weekend's break in Istanbul. You were acting really strange and I thought...'

'I freaked out all right? I freaked out like nobody's business. But then I got over it.'

'Well, maybe now it's my turn to freak out?'

'You're not just freaking out; you're ending something here. You're telling me that you're not in love with me. How do you expect me to still consider a future with you even if you eventually snap out of it? You are burning bridges here.'

An hour later we were in our flat drinking straight vodka in the living room. We were both sitting on the carpet, that famous carpet we had bought from the freaky carpet shop in the Grand Bazaar. Berlusconi was trying to catch his own tail. Berlusconi was our cat. 'Poor cat,' I thought to myself. He's only been here for two weeks and already mummy and daddy are talking of splitting up. Berlusconi is part of a dysfunctional family. He's only three months old, the poor baby. Who's going to take care of Berlusconi if mummy moves out? No, I cannot leave my little boy behind. Berlusconi and I will find a way to survive. I could just picture the two of us stationed outside the main entrance of Harrods on a cold rainy night under a sleeping bag. I would be in dreadlocks and poor Berlusconi would have a nation of fleas on his coat. Maybe he was the sole purpose of me having a relationship in the first place. Like when you decide to keep the baby after a drunken one night stand. He took a deep breath and then said, 'Will you ever be able to forgive me?'

I nodded with a doubting look on my face and replied, 'You need to give me time to adjust to being friends again.'

'Shit, this is getting serious,' I thought. 'Just tell him that you love him.' I turned around to look at him. He smiled back. 'What are you waiting for, just tell him!' 'No, I can't, not yet anyway; I'm not drunk enough.' 'Then drink for crying out loud woman!'

At that moment Berlusconi came to my defence and started biting his left foot. He said, 'Stop it Berlusconi!' but Berlusconi wouldn't listen so he tried to change his position by lifting his right leg up and just as he was doing this, all of a sudden he let out a big loud fart.

I was ready to laugh hysterically but I controlled myself and instead asked, 'How can you possibly fart at a moment like this?'

'I don't know how it happened. It's all his fault,' he said while pointing at little Berlusconi.

'Blame the cat for your own fart. How convenient. It just shows what kind of a person you really are.'

'If it wasn't for him I would've never moved my leg abruptly like that. Now that I've farted, you must hate me even more.'

'You can read my mind!'

'Look at the bright side. At least it doesn't smell.'

I told him that I wanted to be on my own for a while so after giving me a goodnight kiss on the forehead he left and went to bed with an apparent look of guilt on his face.

I spent the rest of the night sitting on the carpet and going to the kitchen to refill my empty shot glass. As I sat there in complete silence, in our nearly empty living room, I kept asking myself the same question. Why wasn't it working?

Maybe all he really wanted was to hear the overrated three word sentence. Although I was still conscious of the fact that I wasn't in love with him, I was also aware that I wasn't ready to let go. Somewhere in the back of my mind I still believed that we could make it work. That if he was ever patient enough and I was determined enough, I could let myself go and actually have a future with him. Around three in the morning when I was finally drunk as a fish and was able to cleanse my system from all my inhibitions I snuggled up to him in bed and said, 'If I didn't love you or care for you I would never have jumped into a relationship with you to begin with. I do love you, you know? As for fireworks; I really don't know. We can try all sorts of ways of improving and enriching our relationship but if it's perfection that you're after forget it. What I've noticed with you is that the moment I become distant or agitated, or grumpy for even a split second, or I'm not up for sex you're put off by me. I am only human you know. I cannot pretend not to show any negative emotions.'

I sighed for a moment and then said, 'Above anything else, I am an individual. An individual who's nowhere near to being perfect. But an individual who wants to grow with you and make herself better with you.' I continued as I held on to his right hand that was embracing me, 'I am not a role model when it comes to relationships. We both have our own issues that we'll probably spend a whole lifetime struggling with. But what I do know is that in order to allow our relationship to flourish we have to be patient and strong enough to let it grow; regardless of whatever problems we face on a day-to-day basis.'

He said, as he was still tightly gripping onto me from behind, 'I need a bit of time to sort everything in my head. Just give me a bit of time.'

The next morning, while he was at work, he called. 'How are you feeling?'

'I've been better.'

'What are you doing?'

'Working on my book as usual. You know, I got a heading for my last chapter. It's called "Fireworks".'

'Fireworks. You're funny. So I gather, this chapter is about me.'

'Do you mind?'

'Not one bit. At least I'll know that I've had some sort of an impact on your life.'

'You might not like what you're going to read. I can be brutally open and harsh about my characters.'

'Fireworks... I think it's a great name for a chapter. Do you know how you're going to end it yet?'

'Nope. Life will show me.'

That same afternoon, while his kids were playing in the living room and he was on the phone in his room, I locked myself into the room next door and started typing away my final chapter.

The next day, in the late afternoon he called me. By then everything had slowly started to sink in. I was lying motionless in bed like a corpse while brainstorming:

OK, let me just analyse my current situation. I am thirty-one years old, unemployed and have been dumped by my boyfriend of just three months. Basically my life is a wreck. I might as well just go ahead and shoot myself. But no, I can't do that to my Mother. I have to put up with this misery a bit longer, well at least until the day she dies.

He said, 'How are you?'

'How am I? Don't ask me such a complicated question.'

Then after a brief moment of silence he said, 'Please forgive me for everything I've put you through in the past two days. I am such an idiot. I guess I just needed to hear you say that you loved me.'

'What?'

'I love you.'

'I don't know if I can ever trust you again,' I responded.

'Please trust me. You have to trust me. I will never repeat the same mistake; never. No more freaking out. That goes for both of us. I'm on my way from work now. Would you care to have dinner with me at Zuma?'

'I don't know if I can get up. I feel really tired.'

'You've got to give me one more chance.'

'Well, I need to take a shower first and transform myself into a human being again. You'd be scared if you saw me right now. Amazing what depression can do to a person.'

'I am sure you look as amazing as ever. Should I pick you up?'

I sighed for a moment and then said, 'No, it's better if we meet there in forty minutes.'

An hour later we were nibbling on a variety of sushi and sashimi while holding hands now and again. He said, 'Maybe I needed to go through something like that. I think this will make our relationship even stronger.'

Then my mobile rang. I looked at him. I wasn't really in the mood to talk to anyone else.

He said, 'Pick it up. I need to make a phone call as well.' And then disappeared. Roughly twenty minutes later he was back at the table with the same funny look on his face that he had had two nights before. I anxiously asked, 'What is it?'

He just shrugged his shoulders.

'What's going on? Who were you on the phone with just now?'

He said that it was his ex-girlfriend. The Brazilian he'd dated for a year right after his divorce.

'And?'

'I'm really sorry for doing this to you.'

'I can't believe this. No, I really can't believe this...'

'I just don't know who I love, what I want, or even who I am any longer.'

'So, you've been seeing her behind my back.'

He took a deep breath and covered his face with both hands and said as he slowly removed both hands from his face, 'I'm going to be real honest with you now. I've never been honest to a woman in my life but I can't do this to you, you're not just any other woman, you're my friend. You're probably going to hate me for it but I feel that I owe it to you.'

'You mean that it gets even worse.'

He nodded.

'I've been seeing quite a number of women behind your back. And it's not just for sex. You see, I've been telling them stories. Giving them hope, the way I've been doing with you for the past three months. I have this uncontrollable desire to make women fall in love with me. I want to be loved.'

'I guess one woman's love doesn't do it for you.'

'I've been like this ever since my divorce. I think I need professional help.'

'I totally agree. But I thought you had finished it with the Brazilian a year ago.'

'I tried to but she's got this power over me. I have a very strange relationship with her.'

'What do you mean by "strange"?'

'You see, well, she's a dominatrix.'

'You can't seem to stop shocking me can you?'

He smiled playfully as if I had just paid him a compliment.

'So how does this dominatrix thing work? Do you lie submissively in bed while she appears wearing black patent knee-high boots, black latex underwear and starts whipping your ass for being a very, very naughty boy?'

'Well, that's a bit clichéd isn't it?'

'I wouldn't know. Then give me an example.'

'But you have to promise not to tell anyone.'

I rolled my eyes and nodded back at him.

'The last time I was with her she screwed me with a strap-on. I really enjoyed it, being overpowered by a woman like that.'

'Now I know what's missing in our relationship. A strap-on!'

'No it's not like that. Nothing is really missing in our relationship and I'm really sorry for putting the blame on you. Like telling you that I can't stand your mood swings and so on. You've been really wonderful with me. I am aware that it's not easy for you to open up your heart to someone new and that you need time to trust and devote yourself to another being. I also know that if you didn't have any feelings for me, we wouldn't be sitting here, having this conversation in the first place. But the truth of the matter is, I just don't have it in me to sustain a normal relationship. At least for now.'

'Wouldn't it have been wiser to come to this conclusion before you called me from the airport three months ago?'

'I thought that we could make it work, that I could make it work.'

'Maybe you should be with the Brazilian instead? I know that your Mother disapproves of her and considers her as nothing but a low class, cheap slut but maybe that's what ultimately does it for you? Who cares what others think? At the end of the day, it's your life.'

'I can never have a future with her.'

'You've been seeing her for almost two years now. She doesn't know a word of Turkish and can just about speak two sentences in English, yet you've been with this woman for almost two years. You were barely able to stand me for three months.'

'I don't know what I want. You see, I've also been seeing this other Turkish girl who lives in Istanbul. The one I was flying over to see when I called you from the airport that day. She's planning to move to London to be with me. Actually I've been together with her for the past four months. She doesn't even know that you exist. If she manages to find work in London she's going to move out here and move in with me. At one point I convinced myself that she was the one, but now I'm starting to freak out, the same way I freaked out with you.'

I was aware that being friends for the past eight years had made it easier for him to confide in me but his blunt honesty was beginning to seriously get on my nerves. I said as I raised my voice, 'Listen to me. No matter what you do, you cannot play with people's lives. You can't play with my life, or anyone else's that you've been screwing up.'

'That's why I'm being open with you.'

'Look at us. We're living in one of the most distinguished areas in town. We're ordering furniture from fucking Harrods for God's sake. We're paying seven hundred pounds for a special breed of cat. We've got it all haven't we?'

I was really getting worked up. I got up from my seat, slammed my hand firmly on the table and shouted, 'But we're too fucking miserable to enjoy it all!'

'Come on, take it easy, everybody's staring at us.'

I pointed my index finger at him and said, 'You know what's really wrong with you? You think that you can solve all your problems with money. The dining table that you just got from Armani Casa can transform your living room. But what about this?' I said as I continued to point my index finger right on top of his heart. 'How do you intend to fix that? By buying off some Brazilian dominatrix or by deceiving people? Is that the best that you can do?'

He was lost for words. I grabbed my bag and made my way to the exit. I knew that if I continued to stay there, there was a high probability that I would punch him in the face. I didn't want to give him the satisfaction.

As I was power-walking on Brompton Road, I felt relieved. Relieved that I wasn't in love with him. I had come close though; really close. For once, my reluctance to open up, my fear of rejection had been of some vital use to me. Did I hate him? Naturally he wasn't my favourite person on the planet right then but above anything else I felt sorry for him. While I had spent the past three months trying to adjust myself to being with someone new and learning to love again, he had spent all his energy lying, deceiving and trying to juggle at least three separate women at one go. And I thought I was being tactical.

I stopped for a second and took out a cigarette from my bag. Then I gazed observantly at my surroundings. There was not a single cloud in the sky. 'What a beautiful evening,' I said to myself. I took a deep breath and started to stroll down Brompton Road. I passed by a group of drunken hooligans in front of a pub that were singing *We are the Champions* like there was no tomorrow. One of them turned his back as soon as he noticed me, dropped down his trousers to reveal his bare, wobbly, white English ass. They all roared with laughter. I smiled back at them. Then another one shouted behind me, 'Come on love, join us for a beer.' As I turned into Fulham Road, I left the sound of loud car engines behind me. I stopped for a second to put out my cigarette. The sharp, cool evening breeze was giving me goose bumps all over. So what now? Where do I go from here? Cuba perhaps?

Come on, don't be silly! If your intention is to escape from corruption don't bother travelling half way across the world. Corruption is everywhere; it's just disguised under a different heading. No regime or religion will ever be able to provide an ultimate solution for human salvation. It can give you various guidelines to follow but it's down to the individual to make the most of it. It's down to me to make the most of it.

Me, me, me!

Whether I choose to be sipping cocktails at a bar in London, or rolling up cigars on my bare, tanned legs at a cigar factory in Cuba, it's all down to me. This power was granted to me at birth. It would be a sin to waste it.

Then out of the blue, I said out loud, 'I love you.'

'Now, where did that come from?' I thought to myself as I raised my eyebrows. I looked around to see if there was anyone close by. Then I smiled awkwardly for having declared my love for myself, as I continued to stroll down Fulham Road. The funny thing is that I really meant it. Like I had never meant it with anyone else before. I looked at the Parliament blue sky with a smile on my face and repeated out loud,

'Yep, it's all down to me.'